Efficient Scientific Writing

Efficient Scientific Writing
Write better papers, faster

Öivind Andersson

Efficient Scientific Writing: Write Better Papers, Faster

Distributed by Amazon
Cover design and illustrations: Öivind Andersson
Contact: oivind.andersson@energy.lth.se
ISBN: 978-91-519-1855-6

Table of Contents

Chapter 1

Boosting your writing efficiency

Scientists write. Period.

It may not be our favorite thing to do. Many would rather spend time in the lab than behind the keyboard, and some even actively avoid the act of writing. Still, we write.

I have often wondered what puts so many PhD students off writing. Some of us probably chose these careers because we realized early on that we were better at math than writing. School may even have left us with a gloomy feeling that writing is a mysterious ability that cannot be learnt. If you add to this the constant pressure to produce peer-reviewed papers, and that everything you write is critically judged by others, it may not be surprising if writing doesn't quite hit the top-ten list of things we like about our job. But writing is a craft that can be learnt. The scientific papers, popular science, and novels you read—they were all written by people who *learned* to write. So can you. With some tools, guidance, and practice you'll develop the skill. Chances are you'll even grow to love it. The aim of this little book is to get you started down that path.

Efficiency is in the approach

I have seen different approaches to writing over the years. Some worked well, some didn't. To convince you that the approach is important, I'll give you a couple of situations from life. For simplicity, I'll call the authors in question student x and student y.

Student x did a small experiment under my guidance when he was only a year from his degree. Knowing how far he had come in his studies, I simply asked him for a draft when he was done in the lab.

After two slow months he handed over a manuscript, and although I was quite familiar with the simple idea behind the experiment, I could barely make sense of what he had written. It wasn't that the text was grammatically incorrect. It just failed to convey any kind of message. He had presented the results in what looked like random order and it was impossible to find any clear conclusions at the end. When I discussed the text with him, there was no doubt that he understood what he had done in the lab. It just seemed like he couldn't explain it in writing. I tried hard to give useful feedback on the manuscript but, as is often the case with a text like this, in the end we had to go back and rebuild the manuscript from scratch.

Student y, on the other hand, was at the beginning of his PhD studies and already about to write his very first paper. As he was worried about his strict deadline, I briefly explained some of the practical techniques in this book to him. When he submitted the paper to the publisher he said, "Now I know it's possible to write a paper in ten days". And he could actually have finished it sooner, because he had spent a part of those ten days reworking the analysis. His paper was accepted for publication with minor revisions.

Looking back, I wouldn't say that student y was inherently a more talented writer than student x. They were both typical engineering students, less interested in writing than in tinkering in the lab. The difference simply lay in the approaches they took to writing. One built his paper bottom-up, putting the details in before he knew how to make sense of them. The other built his paper top-down, starting with the big picture. This helped him write a much better paper in a much shorter time. I'll expand on that approach throughout this book, because it's my firm belief that top down is the only way to write a paper both effectively and efficiently.

As simple as it may sound, I have often found that writing well begins with organizing your work in a series of steps and making sure to finish each step before you move on to the next. Some people call this the writing process, others call it the craft of writing. Whatever you call it, it boils down to developing an approach that guides you through your writing project, and that's what this book is about.

Another benefit of having an approach is that, once you get comfortable with it, you'll probably begin to look forward to writing. That feeling of anticipation comes from realizing that writing is the only thing in science that you have full control over. If you're working in the lab or field, you often have to struggle with faulty equipment and poor conditions. If you are working theoretically, debugging code can eat up big chunks of your time. Writing is different. When you have learned to avoid the common potholes, you predictably end up with a finished text within a predictable time. But to succeed with this, you must take control of the writing process instead of letting the process take control of you. When you gain control, you gain confidence—not only because you finish your drafts sooner, but because they come out much better. You will meet your deadlines with less sweat *and* submit better work.

Efficiency defined

As the word efficiency turns up in the title of this book, I should probably define it before we move on.

It's important to realize that efficiency is not a measure of quality. It's a measure of waste. If you put 100 units of fuel energy into the tank of your car, for example, and measure how much of it goes into actual driving, you'll find that most of it is wasted. When the fuel burns, more than half the energy is lost to the surroundings as heat. About five percent drives useful equipment that isn't really moving the car, like the cooling water pump. Although this is necessary, it's waste from a driving point of view. Another five percent is lost as friction on the way to the wheels, and even at the wheels you continue to lose energy to wind and rolling resistance. In the end, you're lucky if you have used a third of your fuel to move the car. The same is true of your writing. Out of the words you type into your computer, only a fraction will end up in the published paper. Waste is inevitable.

Efficiency, strictly speaking, is defined as the ratio between the output and input of a process:

$$Efficiency = \frac{Output}{Input}$$

The closer this ratio is to 100 percent, the more efficient the process. But some people would rather define efficiency in terms of time. They say that an efficient person needs less time to finish a certain task.

Although this isn't strictly a ratio it's still a good measure of efficiency, because it measures the time we waste doing things that don't improve the result.

We could use any of these definitions to measure a writer's efficiency. We could get a percentage by dividing the number of words in the published paper by the total number of words she put into the pages of all her drafts. Alternatively, we could measure the time she spent finishing her manuscript. Although the latter is less orthodox I would say it's more useful, because it doesn't ignore the fact that waste isn't just wasted words. It's also waste in the form of doing the wrong things at the wrong times. (Incidentally, you may have noticed that the writer is female in this chapter. All readers are not female, of course, and to keep things balanced, I will intentionally switch the genders of our hypothetical readers and writers in alternate chapters throughout the book.)

Whichever definition we choose, the point is that efficiency is a measurable concept. This makes it a useful concept, because we can talk about it without being vague—even if we never actually measure it. If you want to improve your efficiency, you must clearly decrease the number of wasted words and the time you spend doing unproductive things. It's as simple as that.

Now, the inevitable question poses itself: how efficient can you be? For the engine in your car, there is a theoretical limit called the Carnot efficiency. No matter how clever the engineers, they will never develop an engine that beats the Carnot efficiency. Your writing efficiency has a similar limit. There never was an author who sat down to write a scientific paper and put all the right words in the right places right away. A draft always needs revision. In fact, revision is such an important part of writing that it gets its very own chapter at the end of this book. We could of course try to come up with a formula for the theoretical efficiency limit of a writer, but it wouldn't be very helpful. The important thing to realize is that, while some of the waste is inevitable, much can actually be avoided. You will never reach that elusive 100 percent, but you should strive to come as close to them as possible. How to do it? By using strategies that minimize waste.

I started this section by saying that efficiency is not a measure of quality, but you may have noticed my claim that this book is also about writing better papers. We could call this effectiveness. Effectiveness is a less useful concept than efficiency because it isn't readily measurable. Luckily, they aren't independent. As the tools in this book are designed to help you organize your thoughts, they help you to write both better *and* faster—they increase your effectiveness as well as your efficiency.

What this book will help you do

Before we move on, I'd like to stress that what I'm telling you here mostly comes out of my own experiences of writing and helping students write. If you're looking for a book with a lot of theory and citations, this one isn't for you. It's intended to be a hands-on guide. There are plenty of books out there that rigorously discuss the rules of composition and grammar. That's useful at some stages of writing (mostly during the revision, as it turns out), but it isn't sufficient for turning complex ideas into a readable manuscript. Fewer books help you organize the writing process, and fewer still deal with the unhelpful behaviors that keep many of us away from the keyboard until last minute panic hits us. To me, teaching writing by the rules of composition is a bit like teaching architecture by explaining how to connect beams, hoping that the students somehow already understand how to design a building. Writing is something as strange as transferring an idea from your own brain into the brains of others by lining up strings of alphanumerical symbols on a page. While grammar and composition are important for this, they will only get you so far. This book aims to help you organize your writing using a set of practical techniques that remove the obstacles between you and a readable manuscript. It aims to help you develop productive writing habits and shape a text that works.

I will start by discussing three skills that are so important for efficient writing that I will dedicate one short chapter to each of them. The first is knowing *what* to write. This may seem self-evident, but it's all too common for writers to be so results-oriented that they start typing before they know what their message is. The what part of this book discusses the perils of putting everything you did in the lab into your paper. Scientific papers must have a clear focus, and you must prepare for writing by identifying your message and choosing the contents that support it.

When you have decided what to write, your job is to work your findings into a finished, readable draft. For this reason, the next part is knowing *how* to write. The how part presents a number of practical tools and tips that will help you give your text direction.

You also need to handle *time and space* (though not in the Einsteinian sense of those words). The question of when and where to write haunts many who aren't even aware of it—and is actually increasingly difficult to answer due to how office life has evolved. As all project leaders know, time management is a crucial skill if you want to finish a task on time, and that includes writing. You must also make sure to spend your writing time writing—not thinking about writing, pretending to write or (worst of all) blatantly avoiding to write. In the time and space part of this book, we'll look at these unhelpful behaviors and discuss how you can avoid them.

After these general points, we'll turn to the form of a scientific paper. When reading papers, you will have noticed that they are often organized into specific parts that are presented in a certain order. We'll discuss the whys and hows of this format. After that we'll spend a couple of chapters discussing the practical work of shaping your text into a readable, understandable manuscript. As promised, this leads up to a full chapter on the perennially current topic of revision. Finally, we will zoom out again and look at how you can develop your writing skills over time. We will also discuss how writing a PhD thesis differs from writing a scientific paper.

Before diving into the *what* part, I want to stress once more that when I talk about increased efficiency, I'm not talking about increasing your writing speed at the expense of editorial or scientific quality. When it comes to scientific writing, efficiency and effectiveness go hand in hand. Those who write well finish their work faster and produce better papers. And, yes, you can learn how to do it.

Exercise: If you haven't started reading scientific papers yet, now is the time to do it. As you browse the literature in your field, find at least one research paper that you think is well written—something that you wish you had written yourself. We will use it for exercises in the upcoming chapters.

Chapter 2

What to write

Did you ever hear a joke that fell flat? Sometimes, someone tells a joke and forgets something that's needed to get the punchline, or he makes so many digressions that the funny part drowns in unrelated information. We have all experienced the awkward moment that follows when people's gazes are darting around the room to see if anybody else got it.

Saying that scientific papers are like jokes is perhaps taking the comparison too far, but jokes and papers do have points in common. Although your paper doesn't have a punchline, it has a central message, and your job as an author is to give the reader all the information he needs to get that message. Not more. You don't want the message to be lost in a sea of unrelated information.

The message

If you are like most scientists, your first lessons in scientific writing probably came in the form of writing up lab reports. This means that you learned useful parts of the craft early on, at least if your reports followed the standard format of scientific articles. It quickly became second nature to start with the background and theory, continue with methods and results, and finish with a discussion. That's very useful, as long as you understand that, format aside, scientific papers and lab reports are two very different things. They are designed to communicate different messages. One reason why many new PhD students find it difficult to write papers is that they continue to write lab reports.

You write a lab report to show your teacher that you finished (and, let's hope, understood) a practical part of a course. It describes things you did with equipment in the lab and the data you collected. A research paper, on the other hand, isn't primarily about what *you* did— it puts forth a *scientific proposition.*

Repeat that sentence and take it to heart, because it's central to everything we discuss in this book. A paper makes a proposition. It communicates a new insight about the world. By the end of the paper, your reader should have all the information he needs to understand how you reached that insight and judge whether your proposition is sound or not. No more, no less. This boils down to the first rule of scientific writing: Never start to write before you finished the analysis. The analysis gives you the building blocks of your proposition. Before you have them, you don't have the necessary foundation on which to build the rest of your paper. It's as if you were telling a joke. You had better know the punch line before you start.

Some people will protest against this and say that writing is thinking; that you can't know your message before you start to write because writing is what you do to discover what your message is. I agree. Writing is a powerful way to explore ideas, and sometimes the scientific proposition will crystallize out of a text that you're writing, but my point is that this sort of writing really is part of the analysis. Whatever method you use to find out what your message is— statistical analysis, writing, long walks in the woods—when you begin working on your manuscript in earnest, you have to start over. Put the sketch to one side and start with a blank document, because turning your stream-of-consciousness doodles into clear and readable text is a mess.

The question

How do you make your paper convey a clear message? It's quite simple, really. You just make sure that all the conclusions make sense in terms of a specific research question. State the question at the beginning of the manuscript and make sure everything that follows connects it to the conclusions in a logical way. Again, it's like when you're telling a good joke: any information that doesn't build up to the punchline is a potential distraction.

Explicit research questions may be difficult to find in published papers—particularly in applied fields like engineering and medicine—but a good paper always points to a gap in knowledge, and it will be clear that the whole purpose of the paper is to fill that gap. I have chosen to use the term research question in a wide sense that includes any form of problem statement, whether you formulate it as a question or a knowledge gap. The point is, your readers want to know early on where you're taking them, and this leads us to rule number two: Build your paper around one research question and one research question only. If you try to answer several questions in the same paper, your readers will have difficulties understanding what your proposition is. Try telling a joke with several punchlines and you'll see what I mean.

A research question may have several parts. What's important is that, when you add them up, they must amount to a single problem statement. If you find yourself struggling with this, your readers will struggle even more trying to follow your line of argument. If you have difficulties wrapping your material around a single question, it's a clear indication that you should consider writing more than one paper.

So, the starting points when writing a paper can be summed up in the figure below. First find out what your message is. This is your scientific proposition and you should put it at the end of the paper. That's the exclamation mark. Then, formulate the research question that is answered by your proposition and put it at the beginning of the paper. That's the question mark. The rest of the process is drawing the arrow: building a line of argument that leads from the question to the proposition.

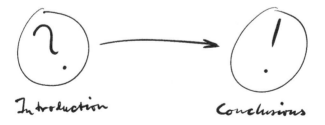

Supporting your message

Back in my undergraduate days, an elderly lady once took me on a trip through the countryside in her small, orange Peugeot. Every time we passed a church, she would point to it and fill me in on details about its history and architecture. This part of the country was dense with villages and her enthusiasm for medieval churches had the little car swaying from side to side, often threatening to leave the road altogether. Looking back, I can't remember where we were going, and I certainly can't remember anything about the churches—the only thing I recall is staring ahead in panic, wondering if we would make it to our destination alive.

Every now and then, an early draft of a paper takes me back to that trip in my youth. They are usually written by students who write their manuscripts at the same time as they evaluate their data. Analyzing your data, you'll often be excited about things that turn up along the way. You make a diagram that looks nice and can't resist the temptation of adding it to the paper. Then you add another, and another, and the line of reasoning sways wildly from side to side instead of staying dead center on the proposition you set out to make.

When adding material as you go along, you almost always end up with a long, incoherent paper. The important information may be there, but it's seldom presented in the clear and concise way we expect of a scientific paper. What's worse is that a thick manuscript often instills a false sense of achievement in the author.

When I suggest making a manuscript shorter, I am often met by looks of bafflement. How could a long paper even be considered to be a problem? The problem is that a big, mixed bag of results makes it difficult for the reader to see clearly what you're trying to say. You could say that your paper reads like a joke with too many digressions. When you reach the punchline, the listener is so distracted by irrelevant information that he fails to understand what's supposed to be funny.

Having someone tell you to go back, cut down on material and start over can be frustrating, especially after putting so much effort into writing a draft. When that happens, there's a natural tendency to blame the reader. If only your lazy supervisor made an effort to read the text more carefully, he would realize how great it is! Well, maybe. But the truth is that an unstructured paper, if it's even published, is rarely read—even more rarely cited. And citations are what people judge you by in this business, whether we like it or not. No matter how interesting your results are, if you don't present them in an accessible way, they stand a slim chance of being noticed. Just as with the failed joke, the problem in this case is not that your readers are lazy.

Here, we arrive at the third rule of scientific writing: Don't put anything in your paper that doesn't support your message. Everything you write should connect the research question to the conclusions in a logical way. Even though you may find your digressions infinitely interesting, they are potentially distracting to the reader. What I mean by supporting your message is that everything in your paper should be there because it's needed. Think of a car: it has four wheels and all of them fill an important function, as will become obvious if you try to take one of them off. Nobody would think you were smarter if you added an extra wheel. Why would you add something that didn't improve the car? The same principle applies to your writing. If a diagram or even a section can be removed without weakening your message, then it's a fifth wheel and it needs to go.

But supporting your message is not only a matter of focusing on the relevant results. It also means explaining how you get from results to conclusions. As a writer, you should provide your readers with two services. You should *show* them the relevant data and *interpret* the data for them. Don't dump plots in your manuscript and expect people to decipher them by themselves. Think of your data as stops on a sightseeing tour and of yourself as the tour guide. Your job is to take your readers along, show them the relevant sights, and explain what they can learn from them. And when you spot a medieval church along the way, turn your gaze away. Plant your hands firmly on the steering wheel and focus on taking your readers safely to their destination.

Why less is more

Why am I so strict about limiting a paper to a single message? Won't your paper be stronger the more interesting results you put into it?

This may seem reasonable at first, but the fact is that readers are just like us; they may read for pleasure, but probably not the papers you and I have written. When they browse the scientific literature, they do it for professional reasons. They have specific questions in mind and want to see from the title and abstract whether a paper is relevant or not. After downloading a selection of the most promising papers, they don't want to find themselves rambling through vague texts that deal with many things in general but nothing in particular. They want concise, readable articles that expand on the titles and abstracts.

Remember that your readers don't owe you any favors. They don't have to read your work, and they certainly don't have to cite it. If you want your work to have the scientific impact it deserves, you must deliver useful information in a useful format. Try to read your text with your readers' eyes. Imagine a reader who wants to get a quick overview of what's been published in a certain area, and that your paper is one of many hits in a literature search. Ask yourself if what you write would motivate that reader to read on or put it aside.

The figure below is a useful illustration of how you should choose what to include in your paper. One of the circles represents what you found out during your investigation, the other represents what your readers want to know, and the part where the two circles overlap defines what's relevant.

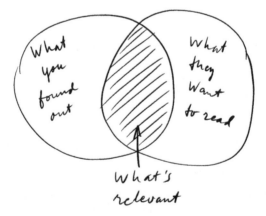

Sometimes it's easy to decide what information is relevant, sometimes it's not. For example, plans might change in the middle of a study. You may have found a more interesting angle on your problem and switched to a different line of attack. Should you then explain to the reader how the scope changed? Most often, the answer is no.

Again, the key is to look at it from a reader's point of view. When you browse the papers from a literature search, do you want to be distracted by authors discussing what they *didn't* study? Probably not. You're looking for information that's relevant to a specific problem. Some writers think it feels a little like lying if they don't explain the whole thought process behind their experiment, but the truth is that the detours and dead ends they encountered on the way aren't necessarily relevant to their conclusions. If they aren't, leave them out. This is how Steven Pinker describes the situation where you don't know the point of what you did until afterwards:

> *An old cartoon captioned "The PhD thesis" shows a little boy firing an arrow into the air, seeing where it lands, walking over to it, and painting a target around that spot. It's not how science should work, but it's sometimes how writing must work.[1]*

So, don't confuse the reader by describing your inner struggle to find out what the point of your paper was. Write about what the data are telling you. Tell the story that begins with your research question and ends with your conclusions. What's relevant is exactly that story, not the other potential stories that you might have told.

Efficiency lesson

Let's wrap this up by repeating the essential points:

First, we have learned to stifle any impulse to start writing a manuscript before we have finished the analysis. Before you know exactly which conclusions you can draw from your data, it's impossible to know exactly what you need to put in the paper to support them.

Second, your paper must answer a research question. One, not many. The question should be stated early in the paper and everything that follows should connect it to the conclusions in a logical way.

The third thing we learned is never to put anything in your paper that doesn't support your message.

Formulating your scientific proposition before you start to write a draft is efficient because it saves you the labors of carving out a clear message from a text that may look like little more than a random collection of data. Aligning your conclusions with a single research question from the start simply allows you to focus on more relevant tasks during the revision process. In short, it's an approach that minimizes wasted words and wasted time. It's also more effective, since it makes it easier for readers to relate your work to their questions—and this increases your chances of being cited.

Exercise: Read the well-written research paper you picked out in the last chapter and look for the problem statement. Is it formulated as a research question or a knowledge gap? Where in the text is the problem statement presented? Is it explicitly or implicitly stated? Then read the text carefully to see if all parts are relevant, connecting the problem statement to the conclusions. Do the authors make sure that you understand how they get from observations to conclusions? How?

Chapter 3

How to write

Writing is done one word at a time. Words are combined to form sentences, sentences are lined up into paragraphs that are stacked into sections and, together, they make up the finished manuscript. At least, that's what it looks like when you read a paper. But is it the best way to write?

We're now delving deeper into the topic of the writing process, which is something you must develop to be able to write efficiently. As Elizabeth George puts it, "Having no process is like having no craft. It leaves you dangling out there over the abyss, a potential victim of writer's block." [2] When you don't know where to begin, process is what gets you started. When your writing doesn't seem to work, process is what gets you back on course. Without process, you're like a train without tracks—you have a load to pull but no means to give it any direction.

So, should writing be done one word at a time? I would say no. Before I explain what I mean, let me digress with an example to make what follows a little clearer.

Compatibility versus completeness

Just after my PhD, I spent a number of years working for a multinational automotive company. At one point the management discovered that the brands in the group used different amounts of time to develop a new car. Interestingly, the brand that used the least time consistently launched better products than the slowest, which always struggled with warranty issues on their new models. How could it be that one company consistently created better cars in what turned out to be half the time? The answer lay in how they lined up the development tasks—an insight that has important implications for how you should write a paper.

A car consists of systems, such as the chassis and the powertrain. The systems, in turn, consist of subsystems. The powertrain, for example, is made up of an engine, a gearbox and the transmission. You can go on and break the subsystems down into components and parts, which is usually the level where the engineers develop the product. Obviously, you have to develop the components before you can combine them into a car.

Intuitively, it makes sense for an engineer to develop a component to completion before he feeds it up to the subsystem level. The problem is that most of the quality issues arise when the components are combined, because the function of a machine relies on how the parts fit together and how energy and information are transferred from one system to another. When a failure is discovered at an interface, the engineers have to go back to the drawing board and reengineer their components. They have to do parts of their job twice.

Now, the secret of the most efficient brand was that they took time to decide how the components should fit together already before the engineers started working on them. As a result, they knew at the beginning that the parts would play nicely with each other when they eventually built a car out of them. By removing the need for reengineering, they had set up a working process that minimized waste.

Although this may seem like a digression, there is a lesson in this story that applies to your writing: If you spend too much time on details before you have worked out the big picture, you run a great risk of having to rewrite large parts of your text before you're done.

As you see in the diagram below, the least efficient brand spent the early phases of a project developing the best components they could; they were focusing on completeness. In the next phase, they tried to combine the components and inevitably ran into issues with compatibility. The most efficient brand, on the other hand, started by ensuring the compatibility and followed up with the completeness of the designs. Looking at the diagram, the two paths between A and B seem to be exactly equal in length. The problem is that the least efficient path forces you to double back several times before you reach B.

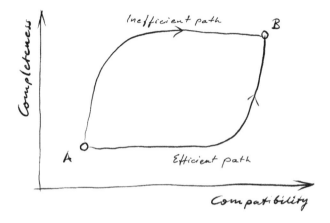

When I described writing in the opening paragraph of this chapter, I described it as a bottom-up process of adding one word at a time. This would be equivalent to developing one component at a time before combining them into systems. As you have probably realized by now, this isn't an efficient approach. In order to minimize waste, you should instead work from the top downwards. You should work on compatibility before completeness. But how?

The answer is that you should ignore your natural impulse to formulate nice sentences and paragraphs before you have settled on the disposition and contents of your paper. In the previous chapter, we started the writing process with the big decisions; settling on a scientific proposition and formulating a research question. You should stay with these broader brushstrokes before you turn to details, because when you hand your first draft over to coauthors and advisors, they will inevitably ask you to move paragraphs around and cut parts out. When you do that, much of the effort that you put into composition will be lost. Your beautiful sentences must be rewritten before they fit together again, and this is wasted work that can be avoided.

The engineering metaphor is more apt than it first seems, because you could really see your text as a machine. It creates a flow where one piece of information leads to the next. When a text isn't working properly, it's usually because you have problems where the parts are supposed to fit together; at the interfaces between sentences, paragraphs, and subsections.

Function before style

You can avoid these problems by drafting your manuscript in three steps, ensuring that you have built function into your text before you turn your attention to style.

The function is about shaping your message and getting it across to the reader—often a fairly complex task. The style is mainly about making the message look good. This doesn't mean that style is unimportant, but I claim that style is less important than function. This is simply because an elegant text that doesn't convey a clear message serves no function at all.

If you aren't convinced that you should focus on function before style, here's an experiment for you. Ask your coauthors for feedback on a finished draft and sort their comments by category. I bet you will get lots of suggestions about the wording, spelling and grammar, but few about the overall disposition and the way you build your proposition. As long as there are text problems that are easy to spot and fix, that's where your friendly critics will focus their attention. It's simply easy to spot errors. Deciding how to convey a complex message is much more difficult, and you must take this into consideration if you want to get the most useful feedback from your friends.

The first step in your drafting process should be a *strawman draft*, which is basically an extended table of contents that lists the headings and subheadings of your paper. Under these you describe the contents of each part and the order in which they will appear as a bulleted list. The strawman also contains the essential figures and plots.

The next step is a *rough draft*, which is a fleshed-out version of the strawman. The bullets are now replaced by running text that contains all the information and references that will go into the final draft, but so far you have not devoted any time to developing finesse.

The final step is a *polished draft*. This is a refined version of the rough draft, something that reads like a manuscript you would consider submitting to a publisher. In other words, you have added style, which should always come last.

These three drafts have three different purposes. The strawman is a tool for structuring your thoughts—a sort of dummy for experimenting with the contents and the order in which they are presented. It's also a tool for generating feedback from your coauthors at an early stage, to avoid large rewrites later on. The aim is to decide on the *contents* and to find a *disposition* that delivers your message in an effective way before moving to the next level of refinement. This draft forces your coauthors to give feedback on the function of the text, simply because it's impossible to comment on the style at this point.

But contents and disposition are just the first step. You must elaborate your paper with explanatory text if it is to make sense to an outsider, and the rough draft is a working document where you formulate your proposition more fluidly. It gives coauthors opportunity to give feedback on your *rhetoric*. Is the line of reasoning clear? Is everything well motivated? Are some parts too long? The key is to stay focused on the message and not sink into the morass of scientific style at this stage.

But if I'm writing, you say, why not add a touch of style right away? Well, most people do, and it usually slows their writing down. The idea of scientific style can be distracting and even paralyzing for novice writers. Knowing that your text will be evaluated by others, you will often find that there is a natural pressure to write something that looks "scientific". Have you ever found yourself grinding out a manuscript, going back to edit and re-edit sentences several times instead of moving on—exchanging all the boring everyday words with fancy, scientific ones until you almost forgot what you were writing about? Then you know what I mean. It takes forever to write a text that way and the result is often incoherent. The truth is that scientific style doesn't come naturally to us, and the obvious way around this is to cold-shoulder any doubts about your text sounding "scientific" enough before your line of reasoning is in place. Focus on formulating your ideas clearly before dressing them up. Focus on function before style.

One of my students realized it was easier for her to write a paper after she had presented her work to an audience in the form of a slideshow. Somehow, explaining it orally made her see how the message should be delivered. If it helps, try to write the rough draft as if you were speaking to an audience. Write in the first person if you like. Focus on what you are trying to say rather than how you say it.

When you have received feedback on your rough draft, the third rewrite is mainly about brushing up the language. This may require substantial work, but drafting in three steps still saves time, since the idea of scientific style won't be so paralyzing when style is all you have to worry about. At this stage, style isn't likely to prevent you from explaining your work clearly.

For this three-step model to work, you must explain it to your coauthors before you start writing. Tell them early on that you're going to give them three types of drafts and that you expect three types of feedback on them. At the strawman stage, you will ignore any comments that aren't related to disposition and content. At the rough draft stage, you want to hear about the logical flow of the text, and you will ignore any comments on wording and grammar before they have read the polished draft. This workflow forces them to comment on *all* the important aspects of your text, not just the style.

Don't write linearly

One of the greatest obstacles to writing clearly is the idea that writing is a linear process; that you will steadily build a finished paper by adding one word to the next. Forget that. Writing something as complex as a research paper is more like a pregnancy than working at an assembly line. It's an organic process.

Perhaps we get the idea of linear writing from the fact that we read linearly. If you're like most people, you probably start reading a paper at the introduction and keep going until you run into the reference list. That's not necessarily the most efficient order in which to write a paper (nor to read a paper, but that's another story). Strange as it may sound, it's often better to start drafting backwards.

If we begin looking at the strawman draft, there's a very good reason why you should start at the end. As I pointed out in the last chapter, everything begins by settling on a scientific proposition which will be presented at the end of the paper. Everything before that must point towards the proposition, a bit like everything in a murder mystery builds up to the climax of finding out who the murderer is.

Most suspense writers know who the killer is when they sit down to write their stories. They know this because they have spent time developing their ideas in a synopsis, planting false suspects and red herrings in the plot, setting up obstacles for the sleuth to overcome before the truth dawns on him and he finally confronts the real villain. They do this because their readers expect the story to make perfect sense when they reach the end. No matter how exciting the story was, if everything doesn't come together in the end, readers will feel cheated. Your strawman draft is exactly like that synopsis. It gives an overview of your line of argument. This is the reason why you should formulate your conclusions before you start writing, because they are the pinnacle that your whole paper strives towards—the scientific equivalent of the identity of the murderer in a whodunit novel.

When the conclusions are in place, take a look at them. Can you see exactly which results and figures you need to show to support them? I thought so. Why not put those results and diagrams into the strawman right before the conclusions, under a suitable heading—like Results? And when the results are there, don't you begin to see how your experimental setup and techniques should be presented for the reader to understand how you got the results? This is a good time to do that, just before the Results section. When you're done with that, you'll see how to explain why you set the experiment up like you did, in order for the whole paper to make sense. This is one of the important things you should explain in the Introduction. This is how you build a strawman draft where all the parts point towards the conclusions. Building up to a scientific proposition is basically as easy as that.

When you move on to the rough draft, it's probably a good idea to begin with the most difficult parts of the paper. The reason is that your energy and enthusiasm will tend to decline over time and it's wise to use them for the intellectually most demanding work. Only you can decide which parts are most demanding for you. For some, it's the discussion, where everything they wrote must come together to form solid conclusions. For others it's the introduction, where they're expected to put the work into a wider context. When you have taken a stab at what you think is most difficult, move on to the second most difficult part and continue until you have written it all. Then read the whole draft from beginning to end to make sure it's coherent.

In some situations, it could make sense to start writing the easiest parts of the rough draft. They typically deal with methods, materials, and experimental equipment, and are often a welcome resort on days when your brain refuses to cooperate despite a looming deadline. I will even stretch it and say that it may be more efficient to start writing some of these parts already during the analysis stage—violating the don't-write-until-you-finished-the-analysis rule—because it will give you something useful to do during those inevitable periods when you're stuck or waiting. What I'm playing at here is the psychology of writing. When you eventually start to write in earnest, the task may seem less daunting if you know that you have already produced a few manuscript pages. You're taking advantage of the energizing sense of having achieved.

The first time that it makes sense to work linearly is when you start working on the polished draft. You now have a raw text material that you're supposed to work into elegantly fluent English. This job is best done in the order that you normally read a paper. You will edit the text, read it to check if it says what you want it to say in the way you want to say it, then re-edit and re-read it over and over until you're satisfied. Some people describe this as the work of two different persons within you: the creative doer who puts words on the page, and the critic who reads and makes judgements. Sometimes, the critic nods approvingly, but most of the time he shakes his head and tells the doer to do better. This kind of roleplaying within ourselves is necessary, because you would never finish if you allowed your inner critic to do all the writing. You would get stuck in details, polishing each sentence to perfection until you lost track of what the text was about. If you kicked the critic out, on the other hand, your text would never make it beyond the incoherent shambles of an early draft. You must let these two sides of you take turns with the text, alternately moving through stages of production and evaluation. It's a slow, painstaking process, and this is why you should save it until you have a functioning line of argument in place.

The overall process is organic because there's already a rudimentary version of the paper when you start writing the rough draft. Just like an embryo has arms and legs, your strawman has a plan for everything from the introduction to the discussion. And just as the embryo grows into a fetus, each part of your paper grows independently as you skip between them, building the raw material for your paper. The idea is to let every part develop at a healthy rate, ignoring the details before you've built a solid foundation for them.

Virtues of the generic manuscript format

Style is not the only distraction you'll encounter. Another common problem, especially when writing conference papers, is that you're sometimes expected to submit your manuscript in a print-ready layout. Usually, this is a pre-formatted two-column template. Now you're not only facing the challenge of writing a good paper, you're also expected to play typesetter. Ah, the distractions that come with it! How do you make sure the figures are located at the correct positions (at the top or bottom of a column) and how do you make the text fill the rest of the columns squarely?

Word processors are designed for putting words into a manuscript, but they're generally quite unsuitable for layout work. Ask a few professional typesetters what software they use and you'll get the point. My firm advice is to put the layout off until you have finished the text. You do this for the same reason that you put scientific style off until you have decided how to present your work—to avoid distractions. Writing is difficult enough as it is, and it deserves your full attention. This is one of the reasons why you should always compose your text in a generic manuscript format. If this is new to you, here's what a professional manuscript looks like:

It has *ample margins*, at least one inch of them, all the way around the text. This means to the right and left as well as at the top and bottom of the page. Inside these margins the text is written with *double line spacing*. Along with the margins, this puts empty space into your manuscript. As we will see, this is helpful in several ways.

A manuscript is also written in a *standard font*. In the old days, this was always Courier 12 pt, which looks like what comes out of a typewriter. These days we tend to use Times New Roman 12 pt. The text is *left-aligned* and paragraphs are separated by a *double linefeed*. Finally, if you want to print the manuscript, print on *one side* of the paper only. That's it. The figure on the next page shows what it looks like on paper.

If you aren't used to writing in manuscript format, I suspect these guidelines will seem arbitrary and quite unrelated to the task of composing a functioning text. So why do I think you should bother with them at all? If we start with why we should put empty space into the text, the original reason was that it made editing easier. People used to write comments and suggestions on the manuscript pages with

Ample margins →

Modern DI diesel combustion systems consist of a multi-hole fuel injector mounted
in the cylinder head and a cavity in the piston where the main part of combustion
takes place. The injector nozzle is normally placed on the cylinder centerline and the
fuel jets emanating from it are directed radially into the cavity. A central injector
location allows an axisymmetric fuel injection and combustion chamber geometry to
be utilized, which facilitates full utilization of the trapped charge.

Double line-spacing

Extra line feed

Aligned left

One reason for placing the cavity in the piston is that it allows a flat cylinder head
surface. This increases the mechanical strength, which is favorable for withstanding
the high peak cylinder pressures prevalent at high loads. Another reason is that the
cavity plays an important role in generating a gas motion that supports the
combustion process. The combustion chamber has a number of characteristic

a red pen. These days, people edit and comment electronically, and this is actually another good reason for keeping the text spacious. As many modern word processors will add comments in the margin every time you move a comma or delete a word, the commented manuscript quickly becomes horribly difficult to overview, especially if it's written in a two-column layout. The less text there is on each page, the less busy the edited document will look.

But the most important reason for making the text spacious is that it makes the manuscript easier to read. If you open a novel at a random page, you'll find that there are usually about 10 to 15 words per line and about 35 lines per page. This is not a coincidence—typesetters know that this combination makes it easy for you to read the book. When your eye reaches the end of one line it should find the beginning of the next without effort. This requires a certain balance between the line length and the line spacing. If you use a font size that fits 10 to 15 words into a line, the line space has to be adjusted so that, on a normal book page, there will be about 35 lines per page. On a manuscript page, there are usually more words per line and this requires more space between the lines in order for the eye to track the text without effort.

If you take another look at the novel, you'll notice that the typesetter has deliberately wasted some paper by not printing all the way to the edge of the page. The reason is not that you're supposed to write comments there (although you could if you wanted to), but that it's easier to read if there's a bit of space around the text. It's simply more pleasing to the eye. If you're not convinced, make an experiment. Take a text and print it out in a small font with as small margins and as small line spacing as possible. Then print the same text using the manuscript format I described above. Which is easiest to read? Looking at the first version, you may feel overwhelmed by the text, whereas you will probably feel that the standard manuscript almost invites you to read.

These may be good reasons for putting empty space into the text, you say, but limiting your choice of font is surely an unforgiveable violation of a writer's creative freedom? Times New Roman has some advantages, though, which is the reason it has become a standard font. First of all, it has a neutral appearance and is easy to read. One feature that makes it easy to read is the serifs—the little horizontal lines at the bottom of the characters—which connect the text and guide the eye. If you open up a random book you'll find that, almost without exception, the body text is printed in a serifed font. Times New Roman is also useful when mixing equations and Greek characters with normal text. This is because it has the same typeface as the Greek characters in the font Symbol, which is why equation editors often use these two fonts to display mathematical formulae.

Finally, the reason for printing on one side of the paper is simple. It makes it possible to put any two pages face up in front of you, for example if you want to look at a figure that's discussed on a different page. Some publishers even demand that you put all the figures and captions separately at the end of the manuscript. Editors and reviewers can then keep a stack of figure pages beside a stack of text pages and refer easily from one to the other while reading.

In summary, some of the reasons for using a generic manuscript format have to do with efficiency. You simply don't want to be distracted by typesetting problems when composing text, and you don't want to make the revision process more complicated than necessary. Some students I've met will refuse to alter a sentence if it makes a figure jump to the next column and mess the manuscript up. Avoid being sidetracked by layout problems like these and use the word processor for its purpose. When you prepare figures, prepare them in separate programs intended for that, save them as image files and insert them into the manuscript.

Other reasons for using the manuscript format have to do with savviness. It's designed to keep the text clean and readable, making it easier to work with the paper. It makes the manuscript look professional—and you want to submit something that looks professional.

Finally, since we are on the topic of submitting your work, there is one practical point to consider before you put anything at all into your manuscript: where to send it. Scientific publishers demand that your manuscripts follow their preferred styles. To make this easier for you, they publish author instructions on their homepages. Take some time to read them. Some journals have a maximum word count, for example, and that's obviously useful to know at an early stage. Journals also use different styles for references and in-text citations, so checking the author guidelines of your journal before you start writing will probably save valuable time before you're finished.

Efficiency lesson

To actively avoid wasting words and time, work top-down. Build function into the text before you turn your attention to style. The three-step drafting process I propose in this chapter helps you do that. Efficient writing is not a linear process—it's organic.

Exercise: Read the published paper that you worked with in the last chapter and, for each paragraph, write a short statement describing what the paragraph does. Does it motivate the use of a technique, for example, or explain how an instrument works, or describe what's shown in a diagram? Then open a new document, put these statements down in a bulleted list under the headings and subheadings of the paper. You have now extracted a strawman draft from a journal article and should have a good idea about what your own strawman drafts should look like. You can also ask yourself why the contents come in the order chosen by the authors. Would you have chosen a different disposition? If so, why?

Exercise: Open a new document and format it as a standard manuscript, with ample margins, double line spacing, and Times New Roman 12 pt as the default font. Save it as a template and use it *every time* you start working on a new text.

Chapter 4

Time and space

Newton's law of inertia states that a body in motion continues with the same speed and direction unless acted upon by an outside force. This law applies in all sorts of situations—your writing included. In this chapter we'll take a look at how you create momentum when writing, and how you avoid losing it.

The art of not losing momentum

Have you ever failed to finish an important task because you were constantly interrupted by outside forces and never quite got up to speed again before the next interruption? Welcome to the life of the modern professional. Today, we are all expected to keep several balls in the air. The irony is that juggling several tasks is considered efficient, despite the scientific evidence showing that our brains are quite unsuited for multitasking. The vast majority of people who work on more than one task at a time perform worse than if they finished them one after the other, at least with tasks that require a minimum of concentration.[3]

The truth is that you aren't truly multitasking when doing several things at once—you're constantly switching between the tasks, and each time you switch you need a little time to refocus. In productivity terms this is called setup time. When you're interrupted more frequently, the setup time becomes a growing share of the total time you need to complete the job. It's a bit like stopping an express train at each station along the way. Apart from the time needed to pick up new passengers, time and energy are lost to accelerate the train after every stop. The whole trip takes much longer, and inertia is an important part of the explanation.

Here's a typical writing situation for you. Imagine yourself sitting in your office writing your next paper. Your thoughts have finally connected to one another and you know exactly where you are headed with your text—you're in the flow. At this point, your scientific advisor knocks on the door, asking if you have a second (it's always just a second). You are pulled from your flow and your thoughts, trying to understand what he is talking about. Of course, the one-second interruption evolves into a chat (it always does), and by the time you're done you go back to your manuscript with the inevitable question: Where were you?

If you look at the diagram below, you'll see what just happened. When starting on a task that requires concentration, it takes some time to focus enough to work efficiently. This level of focus is drawn as a horizontal dashed line. Above this line you're in the flow. When your advisor comes into the room your concentration drops, not only below the line, but all the way down to zero. This is because you suddenly have to think about something completely different. And when he leaves, you have to work your way up the slope of the curve again. People who have studied this say that you often need more than 20 minutes before you reach full focus again, and this doesn't include the time you spent thinking about that other task.[4]

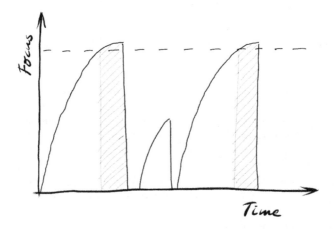

Setup time is waste. It increases your cycle time without adding anything productive. If you multiply the number of interruptions in a day by 20 minutes, you'll probably find that setup time makes up a substantial part of your working week.

If you look at the curve again, you'll notice that I have shaded the parts where you are actually working efficiently. Surprisingly short, aren't they? There are basically two ways to increase the time you spend in those shaded regions. One is the brute force method of working longer hours. This doesn't improve your efficiency; it just increases your workload. The other is to avoid unnecessary setup time. If you can accomplish that, you will produce more in less time, and this is the definition of working efficiently.

Zen and the art of writing a paper

Avoiding setup time is sometimes easier said than done, especially if you're working in an office. One of my favorite TED talks is Jason Fried's *Why Work Doesn't Happen at Work*.[5] He explains how offices are equipped with computers, meeting rooms, internet access, and other features that are intended to increase our efficiency. Yet, when he asks people where they go to get things done, they tell him they go to cafés, libraries, or even home. Nobody goes to the office to finish important work. Their explanations boil down to what Fried calls the M&M's: meetings and managers that prevent people from focusing on their work by chopping the day up into fragments. The more your job requires thinking, the more harmful the M&M's will be for your productivity.

Unfortunately, meetings and managers are not the only disturbances in modern offices. The worst is probably a third M— your e-mail.

Before the invention of e-mail, sending messages cost money. It would also take at least a day to move them from sender to addressee. As inefficient as this may seem, snail mail had its advantages. Since letters were delivered once a day, you would read them once a day, and not every other minute as you tend to do with e-mail. After spending some time reading and replying to these letters, you would spend the rest of your working day—working. Due to the cost, you would send letters only to the people concerned, and since they were a slow way of communication, you would generally put some thought into writing them. This meant that when people sat down to read a letter, they could be pretty sure it was worth reading.

E-mail, by contrast, is cheap and fast. With neither cost nor effort attached to our communication, volumes go up and the quality inevitably drops. These days, people spend more time than ever with their correspondence. Sadly, much of this time is used to figure out whether the information they receive is relevant or not.

The first thing you can do to avoid these constant interruptions is to turn off the sound that tells you a new message has dropped in. Better still: turn the whole e-mail client off. When you get over the eerie feeling of being cut off from the world, you'll realize that you can actually turn it back on after your writing time is over.

Plan the time you spend with e-mails. Perhaps one hour in the morning and one hour in the afternoon is reasonable? Who knows, really focusing on e-mails at those times may even make you more efficient at handling your inbox. At any rate, the key to preventing e-mails from taking over your writing time is to read and process them when *you* choose to do so, not the very moment they drop in. Needless to say, this also goes for checking your social media flow or the news sites every time you have a second to spare. A compulsion to constantly find out what other people are doing keeps you from focusing on what *you* are doing.

The point is that writing efficiently requires uninterrupted time. When you have created that time, even if it's just an hour here and there, the key is to stay zen—to be present in the moment and deepen your focus.

Where and when to write

Interruptions by e-mail and other media is something you can control yourself, but meetings and managers are more difficult to avoid since most of us are expected to be in the office, at least during some designated core hours when most meetings are scheduled. This is where strategic management of your time becomes important.

Take some time to reflect on how your workplace makes you feel at different times of day. Experiment with coming in earlier some days, or leaving later on other days. When do you feel relaxed and when do you feel restless? How you feel could be a question of how many colleagues are around, but also of what they are doing at different times of day.

The early morning is often the least busy time in offices, and usually a good time for writing. If it is, try to schedule your day to take advantage of this. You may even want to block some time in your calendar to make yourself unavailable for meetings in the mornings. If you can't, early mornings at home, before anybody else has gotten out of bed, may be your best shot at getting some productive writing done. Or late at night when your chores are done and things tend to calm down. Time management is partly about avoiding distractions, but also about harvesting your energy when it's available. Are you an early bird or a night owl? Don't fight it—write when your ability to focus is at its peak.

Another important aspect of managing your writing time is realizing that it isn't limited to the moments when you are working at your keyboard. Writing involves solving various kinds of problems and your brain is processing them at all times—even as you sleep. Try to take advantage of the time you spend waiting for the train, taking a shower, emptying the dishwasher, or waiting in line at the grocery store. You will probably find that it's easier to solve certain writing problems when you have some distance to your text, because you are at leisure to consider your options without the pressure to start punching the keys again.

That said, I would like to stress the importance of not spending every minute of the day thinking about your writing. You also need time to refresh and energize yourself, whether it is by jogging, spending time with friends, or reading a great novel. If you wear yourself out, your writing will suffer. Being unproductive is actually an important part of being productive.

In this chapter, we have talked about how crucial time management is for your efficiency. But it's not everything. In the next chapter, we will see that it must be combined with productive writing habits to yield good results.

Efficiency lesson

To make your writing time as efficient as possible you must avoid interruptions—both voluntary and involuntary ones—and commit to being fully engaged with your writing. Voluntary distractions are often just as problematic as the involuntary ones. They consist in anything you do during your designated writing time that isn't writing. When you find yourself reading the news or checking your Instagram feed, it's often a message from your subconscious self, telling you it's trying to escape the act of writing. Even sourcing information for your paper instead of writing can be a voluntary interruption. To write efficiently, you should collect the information you need *before* you write. If you still find that you miss something important, it's better to make a note of it—perhaps within brackets in the text—and continue writing. At the end of your designated writing time you'll probably have several notes to check and, *voilá*, you just avoided unnecessary setup time both in your writing and your information search.

Exercise: Are you often interrupted by outside forces at your workplace? What are those interruptions? List them, think of ways to manage or avoid them, and experiment to see what works best.

Exercise: Think about your ability to focus. Is it better at certain times of day? Experiment with writing at those times. How does it affect your efficiency?

Exercise: Try switching your e-mail client off after you have gone through your inbox. Don't switch it on until you expect to have a sufficient number of unread messages to make it worthwhile to spend time on them. How does this affect your ability to focus?

Chapter 5

Creating productive habits

Have you noticed how some things suddenly seem more important when you have a long text to write—like cleaning the office or sorting your paperclips? You can see so many reasons to put writing off. Writing is hard, especially when you can't find the inspiration, and when what you write doesn't read like a published paper you may even wonder if you have the talent to do it. These negative emotions aside, writing a paper can seem overwhelming. It's natural to think it requires long stretches of time—something that you'll rarely find floating around in your calendar. This tips the balance. If writing is such a gruesome job and you can't expect to get anything done anyway, why not do something useful instead? Sort those paperclips, maybe.

The saboteur within

If you recognize this behavior, you're not alone. Most students procrastinate, and they procrastinate more with writing than with other tasks.[6] Writing creates a pressure to perform, because every text you write as a PhD student is evaluated by others. This often leaves you with a feeling that whatever you do will result in negative criticism. Who wouldn't be put off by that?

Your feelings affect your actions. If you feel bad about writing, no wonder those paperclips suddenly seem to deserve your full attention. When the deadline approaches and you're *forced* to work on your text, you'll probably become absorbed in sourcing information, checking citations, or formatting text—tasks that keep you working on the paper but aren't really writing. Sometimes, their only purpose is to keep you from the dreadful act of composition. They are what psychologists call displacement activities.

Since these behaviors kill your writing efficiency, you need to find ways to avoid them. The first step is to understand that you don't procrastinate because writing is difficult. It *is* difficult, but so are other things that you *don't* put off. Writing is no more overwhelming than working in the lab, for example, and you always finish your experiments, even though it means spending weeks in the lab. So why wouldn't you finish your paper? You procrastinate because of false beliefs about writing. These beliefs include the ideas that it's impossible to write without inspiration, that writing is about dumping something that's ready in your head into a manuscript, and that when you do, the text is supposed to come out looking like a finished paper. Let's look at these beliefs in turn.

We need to get one thing straight from the start: it's possible to write without inspiration. In fact, you must. Most creative people testify that inspiration comes from being productive, though we tend to think it's the other way around. When asked where he gets his ideas, famed novelist Ian McEwan says they come when he's working. It's just a question of showing up at his desk every morning.[7] Stephen King says writing is just another job, like laying pipe or driving long-haul trucks. There's no point in waiting for the muse, he says. Your job is to make sure the muse knows where you're going to be every day from seven 'til three. If he does (King's muse is apparently a guy), sooner or later he'll show up, chomping his cigar, making his magic.[8] Pablo Picasso allegedly said that inspiration exists, but it has to find you working. These geniuses all agree that inspiration doesn't grow out of thin air; it grows out of your work.

Message received. You put your butt in the chair, your hands on the keyboard—and immediately draw a blank. How are you supposed to write if you don't have a clear vision of the paper ready in your head? Some people see writing as some kind of brain dump. They can spend weeks just thinking about their paper, not writing a word. The truth is that structuring all the ideas that go into a paper is such a complex task that doing it in your head is not only inefficient—it probably exceeds the cognitive capacity of the human brain. Just like a baker puts his ingredients into a bowl and processes them before he can knead them into dough, you have to put your ideas onto the page before you can work them into a readable text. The manuscript is the vessel that makes it possible to work with your text. No matter how long you think, you'll never feel ready unless you start writing. And you know this, at least if you ever faced a tight deadline. There's nothing that boosts your productivity like a deadline.[9]

Another important point is that if your text doesn't come out looking like the finished paper, it doesn't mean you can't write. Some people think that your ability to write is based on talent. Few things are as frustrating as that idea. Talent is a great asset, of course. It's something that you can pull out of your sleeve to impress people, but here's the thing: Talent is no substitute for craft. You aren't born with craft. It's something you learn. Even the most talented authors, athletes, and actors spent years and years practising technique before they were able to do what they do and make it look easy. It never was easy. The craft of writing is learnt by reading, reflecting, trying things out, and getting feedback. Gradually, you will grow into it.

But what if your text reads like it's written by an amateur? Well, sometimes it does—especially in the beginning—and it doesn't matter, because you don't have to show it to anybody until you decide to do so. All competent writers revise their texts before they let anyone look at them. I once heard Anna Jansson (a successful Swedish suspense writer) say that she starts every day rewriting what she wrote the day before. This takes the strain out of her creative process, because she knows that what she writes doesn't have to be perfect— she'll improve it later. Try that approach. When the blank page seems to mock you, tell yourself that your job is to produce a raw material. It will probably come out as a poor text and that's fine, because a poor text can be revised into a good one, but there's nothing in the world you can do with no text at all.[9]

In summary, avoiding procrastination starts with changing your beliefs about writing, and there is only one way to realize that all of these beliefs are in fact false. That's to write. Even when you don't feel like it, even when you don't feel ready, and when your confidence fails. Shut your inner critic up and just write. Put your ideas onto the page as simply and clearly as you can. Don't be sidetracked by considerations of style. That comes later. Write, and you'll realize that writing—not thinking about writing—is what gets writing done.

Finding your writing snack

If you were training for a marathon, you'd never start with the whole distance at once. You would begin with a few miles and gradually increase the stretch. Trying to make the whole distance would be doomed to fail and probably put you off long distance running for good. Shorter distances, on the other hand, would gradually increase your capacity and let you finish each round feeling that running is something you can do.

Most people who write their first paper do the exact opposite of this: they devote whole days to the job. This is a bit like running a marathon, because long writing sessions tend to leave you drained. Although your level of focus increases during the first minutes of writing, it eventually drops as you get tired. At the end of a full-day session, these people leave the desk sore-eyed and tired. Dragging themselves back to the keyboard the next day is as hard as dragging wounded soldiers back to the front. The more you associate writing with that empty, worn-out feeling, the more you condition yourself to become a master procrastinator.

The recipe is to spend a little time writing every day. You'll be surprised at the progress you make over a week. In fact, studies have shown that people who write a little every day produce more peer-reviewed papers over a year than people who pile their writing up in big heaps.[10] Just as each round gets a runner closer to making the whole marathon, any time you spend writing will get you closer to finishing your paper.

How long is a little then? Well, it depends on who's writing. If your focus begins to drop after one hour, it's a signal you shouldn't write for much longer than that. For some, 45 minutes is the limit, others can go on for more than an hour. Rowena Murray (who popularized the term "writing snack") says that anything up to around 90 minutes can work.[11] Find your ideal snack by experimenting to find out how your energy waxes and wanes during a session.

Then you must remember that the snack is just a stretch of time. To fill that time with useful work, you need to set goals for it. You can hardly overestimate the importance of the goal. Without something to aim for, the only thing you can compare your progress to is the overall goal of finishing the paper. In that perspective, what you wrote will probably seem inadequate. It's important to set a reasonable goal.

How many words do you think you can write in, say, 45 minutes? The only way to find out is to try.

In the figure below, you see that your focus drops below the shaded "flow zone" at some point. If that's the end of your writing snack, you will finish it feeling that you have achieved what you set out to do without being exhausted. If you don't set a goal for your writing session and keep on writing until the focus curve hits zero, you will both feel drained and unhappy with what you achieved. That will make it more difficult to work up the enthusiasm for writing the next time you sit down. This, in a nutshell, is the idea behind writing in snacks.

Some people find it difficult to just write, even if they have a goal and know what they're supposed to write about. If you're one of them, a little warmup exercise called freewriting can help you get into a more productive frame of mind. Begin by creating a new document and decide what to write about. Then set a timer to 10 minutes and keep writing until the alarm sounds. It's crucial not to stop. You can't go back and edit what you just wrote and you can't stop to think about what to write next. Whenever your brain goes blank, just continue typing, writing "if I knew what to write, I would write…" and explain the general idea before you move on.

Most people who try this for the first time have two reactions. First, they are surprised at how much they can write in 10 minutes. Second, they are usually surprised at how badly they can write. That's fine, because the point of this exercise is not to produce great text, but to get into a productive mood. Freewriting is the writer's equivalent to the athlete's warmup before a game—it loosens up the knots in your brain and gets the energy flowing. You might use parts of what you wrote later, or you may throw all of it away. It doesn't matter, because freewriting lets you experience what it's like to just write, and this will rub off on the writing session that follows. It'll make it easier to get into the flow once you start writing for real.

If you're facing a deadline, it may be hard to convince yourself to freewrite and write in short snacks. After all, you have a big job to finish and you need to finish it fast! Well, maybe, but isn't the reason why you find yourself in this situation spelled procrastination? If you don't start writing in time, the work will inevitably pile up in front of you and become more unsurmountable with each passing day. Be that as it may, binge writing still isn't the solution to your problem. It will only put you back in the vicious circle of exhausting yourself and not feeling up to the job the next time you need to write. Like so many good things, writing is best savored in small snacks.

Here's what to do when the deadline is approaching. Stick to your snack. When it's over, take a break. Get out of your chair, move around, pour a cup of strong coffee—you could even do something completely different for a while to release the tension in your mind. When you feel fresh again, sit down. Set a new goal, start a new snack, and repeat for as long as your energy allows. Not longer. But most importantly, start writing in time.

Efficiency lesson

In the middle of Monty Python's movie The Meaning of Life, a lady suddenly appears seated in a red armchair, saying "Hello, and welcome to the middle of the film." You have now reached this book's equivalent of that scene. In the first five chapters I have discussed strategies to increase your efficiency as a writer. In the next five we will look closer at how you approach the text itself in an efficient way. Before we get to that, let's repeat the four key points we have covered so far (but without the bizarre Find the Fish sequence from the Python movie):

The first point is that efficiency is about minimizing waste. This starts with knowing what to write and—just as important—what *not* to write. A paper is not a lab report describing what you did in the lab. It puts forth a scientific proposition, and all the contents are supposed to support that proposition. With this insight, you avoid waste in the form of writing text that has to be removed later on.

The second point is to create your text top-down; to settle on contents and disposition before you start shaping elegant sentences. This avoids waste by making sure that the line of argument works before you put effort into the details. If you work bottom-up—finishing the text of each paragraph and section before you move to the next—much of what you write has to be rewritten when you revise the text, move parts around, expand on some parts and take others out.

The third point is to manage your time. You can't write efficiently if you are constantly interrupted—and it's just as bad to interrupt yourself as being interrupted by somebody else. You need strategies to avoid intrusions into your writing time by meetings, managers, e-mail, social media and so on.

The final point is to avoid procrastination and displacement activities. As we learned in this chapter, it's often our own unhelpful behaviors—not the difficulty of writing itself—that keep us from writing.

In the remainder of the book, we'll deal with how we, through an iterative process of writing and revising, gradually shape the raw material we have written into something that's readable for an outsider. The first step is to look at the form of a scientific paper.

Exercise: Try 10 minutes of freewriting as a warm-up exercise, to shut your inner critic up and put yourself into a productive mode. Then reflect on the experience. How much text did you produce? More than expected? Do you feel differently than after a normal writing session? Describe how and why. Continue to use a few minutes of freewriting as a warmup, especially if you have writer's block.

Exercise: The next time you sit down to write, try to keep track of how your focus increases to a peak and then gradually drops again. How long does it take? Think of this time as your writing snack. Whenever you write, write for this long and then take a break or work on another task before you write again.

Exercise: Before you sit down to write, set a specific goal for what you want to achieve during your writing snack. After your snack, evaluate how well you did. Was the goal realistic? Were you focused? Adjust your goal and stick with your writing snack over a couple of weeks. See the text grow along with your confidence.

Chapter 6

The form of a scientific paper

Writing a good paper begins with doing your housekeeping—putting every piece of information under the heading where it belongs. As self-evident as this may seem, it's more common than you think to see early drafts where some of the background theory has ended up under the experimental setup, or where parts of the setup are described in the results section. Reading a paper like that is a bit like trying to cook in a kitchen where all the pots have been stowed in different cabinets. You could easily spend more time looking for pots than you spend cooking. In this chapter we'll talk about the different sections of a paper and what they are supposed to do for the reader, but we'll also look at a part of the scientific form that beginners sometimes plainly ignore: standards for in-text citations and references. Before we get to that, let's start with the first thing that meets a reader's eye.

Coming up with a good title

Don't underestimate the importance of the title. Although it may not be the first thing you write (for me, it's usually the last), it's what gives your reader his first impression of your paper. It's crucial to find a single phrase that catches his attention.

Ideally, the title is short, but still specific enough to tell the reader exactly what topic you'll cover. With few exceptions this makes the title slightly longer than ideal, and I'm afraid that's something we have to live with. A reader who's looking for papers on, say, gas engines will probably pass a paper over if the title only mentions engines. Readers have specific interests and we have to adapt to that. Apart from being specific and short, the title can come in many forms. It may be a simple statement of the central observations, as in these examples:

Female choice selects for extreme tail length in a widowbird

Caspase inhibition reduces apoptosis and increases survival of nigral transplants

Sometimes, the central research problem makes a good title in itself:

Identification of the social and cognitive processes underlying human cumulative culture

If the paper is built around the characterization of a process, a substance or some other object of study, the title can be a simple statement of this:

Studies on the chemical nature of the substance inducing transformation of pneumococcal types

Effects of gas density and vaporization on penetration and dispersion of diesel sprays

Many papers are built around a theoretical interpretation of results. If so, the title may mention the theory or simply state the hypothesis tested:

Human evolution out of Africa: the role of refugia and climate change

Independent functions of viral protein and nucleic acid in growth of bacteriophage

Some papers describe a method that has been developed. If so, the title may just state what the method is used for:

Near infra-red chemical species tomography of sprays of volatile hydrocarbons

The ABCDE of writing: coaching high-quality high-quantity writing

You will have realized how important a good title is if you ever searched the literature. The person making the search chooses keywords to be matched with specific parts of papers (usually the title and abstract) and the search engine returns lists with titles of papers that match his keywords. If you're lucky, your paper will show up somewhere on that list. If you want people to read and cite your paper, they must understand from the title whether your paper is worth a closer look or not. Taking a closer look usually means reading the abstract, which is a condensed version of your paper—much like a movie trailer is a condensed version of a motion picture—and if that confirms their positive impression, they will probably download the entire paper and read it.

Here's the point: the step when they download your paper is where your chances of getting a citation increases from exactly zero to a positive value. The magnitude of that positive value will increase in proportion to how relevant your findings are to the reader, and to how well you write (which is the topic of this and the upcoming chapters), but also—crucially—to how well you pick your title. Although I don't have any evidence to prove it, I dare to state that most citations begin their lives as an interesting title showing up in a literature search.

The IMRaD format

Nobody who has read a scientific paper could have missed that they almost always deliver their contents in more or less fixed sections that come in a fixed order. It's important to understand how this format helps you to deliver your message—and your readers to understand it.

Although there are slight variations between journals in different fields, most journals in the natural, engineering and medical sciences use some version of the now classical IMRaD format. IMRaD is an acronym formed from the standard headings of the format: introduction, method, results, and discussion. As I said, the IMRaD format is not used in all fields, and some journals are even beginning to move away from it, but the format is still relevant enough to be considered common knowledge.

What's the use of a standard format? Imagine that you're going through a pile of papers to find something that's of particular interest to you. You probably won't read each paper from beginning to end, but you'll skim certain parts to see if the paper is relevant or not. I often go straight to the conclusions after reading the abstract, for example, and then move on to other parts. Considering that this is how people approach a paper before they read it carefully, a convention for putting certain information in certain places can be very helpful.

If we start by looking at the *introduction*, this is where you set the scene for your investigation. It tells the reader where you are, where you're going and why you want to go there. To show the reader where you are, you must explain what the current state of knowledge is. You discuss and cite the scientific literature in your field, focusing on papers that are of key importance to your investigation. This is why the introduction usually contains most of the references in a paper. Explaining where you're going involves showing your readers a gap in the current knowledge and telling them how you aim to fill it. You present your research question or problem statement. The research question is not necessarily formulated as a question, and it may take on different shapes depending on the field you're in. It could involve an hypothesis that you will test with your experiment, or a practical problem that you want to solve. It could describe a need to get more or better data about a particular phenomenon, or the need to discuss the implications of a certain theory. It could also involve the need to develop a new method of some sort. The important part is that the question should represent a gap in the current knowledge—a gap that you intend to fill with your paper. In the introduction you also outline how you intend to answer the question and tell your readers why it's important to do so.

Another purpose of the introduction is to present your scope. Your research area probably has subareas and the scope is simply a description of which subarea you have focused on. The point is that focusing on a specific problem area inevitably means that you intentionally ignore other, similar areas. This must be clear to the reader. If not, there's no way for him to know if what you have written matches his particular interests.

John Swales has formalized the structure of a successful introduction into the following three "moves", or chunks of text. Each move simply states what you are supposed to say in that chunk of text:[12]

1. Establishing a research territory
2. Establishing a research niche

3. Occupying the niche

In the first move, you establish the *territory* by showing that your general research area is important, central, interesting, problematic, or relevant in some way. I will use a paper on the evolution of color pattern in guppies to exemplify these moves,[13] and here is how this paper shows that the research area is important:

> *All too often in evolutionary biology we are led to speculate or infer the mode of action of natural selection; we usually do not know why some individuals are more adaptive than others. Very often attempts to measure natural selection are unsuccessful, leading to heated arguments about the relative importance of selection, genetic drift, and epistasis in evolution.*

Another part of establishing the territory is to introduce and review items of previous research in the area:

> *It is no coincidence that most of the successful studies of natural selection have dealt with animal color patterns; it should be obvious which color patterns are more adaptive in the presence of visually hunting predators. The adaptive significance of warning coloration and mimicry of distasteful species has been worked out* /several citations/.

In the next move, you establish a research *niche* by establishing a gap in the previous research, or a need to extend previous knowledge in some way:

> *Most field and experimental studies have shown that the overall color or tone of inconspicuous species matches or approximates the background* /several citations/, *but they treated species with solid colors or have ignored color pattern. [...] Some striking examples of color pattern polymorphisms remain largely unexplained, for example in Partula and Cepea* /citations/.

Finally, in the last move, you *occupy* the niche you have established by outlining the purpose of your study, for example like this:

> *The purpose of this paper is to show how various aspects of color pattern are moulded by natural selection.*

In this last move, you can also list research questions or hypotheses. Sometimes, you also list your principal findings there.

In summary, the introduction should answer the following questions:

- What field does this research belong to?
- What particular problem area have I focused on?
- What scientific question do I aim to answer?
- Why is it important?
- In what sense will I advance our knowledge about it?

As you see in the examples above, the introduction works like a lens that zooms from a wide-angle view to a detail. It should start with a general picture of the field and gradually move closer to the specific topic of your investigation. Don't fall into the trap of going too general, though. If your paper starts with "Since the dawn of man", for example, you have probably zoomed out too far. Try to start wide, but hint at what the paper will be about already in the first few sentences, as in the guppy example above.

When you have answered these questions, the *method* section explains your practical approach to answering it. How did you design your experiment? Which data did you collect and how did you collect them? Sometimes, especially in the medical sciences, the section is called *methods and materials*, and includes a description of chemicals and other materials you used for it.

If you made a laboratory experiment, this section is where you describe the experimental setup in detail. It should cover all parts of the measurement system, including instrumentation, measurement object, and measurement procedure. If you made a field study, you describe the site and the objects or organisms that you studied there.

When working empirically, it's always important to consider background factors and sources of noise. The method section is where you explain how you tackled them by designing your experiment in a particular way, specifying a data collection plan, and describing how you processed your data. Did you use a control group, for example? Which variables did you measure? How many times did you replicate your measurements and which statistical tools did you use to analyze the data? Details like these must be described carefully enough for your readers to judge if your data are of sufficient quality to support your conclusions and, if needed, repeat your study.

The next section covers the relevant *results*, meaning all the evidence that your conclusions are based on. Here, you give an honest and objective description of how well the data support your claims, including any important negative results. Present your key results in a logical sequence without interpretation and use figures and tables to support your message. Figures are especially important, as it's often easier to see patterns graphically in diagrams than in text or numbers.

The *discussion* part is sometimes separate from the results, sometimes merged with it. Whatever you choose, its purpose is to explain how the results answer your research question. This is where you define your scientific contribution. Just as the introduction can be seen as a lens zooming in from a general picture of the field to your specific investigation, let the discussion zoom back out and put your results into a general context. The discussion is based on the main conclusions you listed at the end of the strawman draft, which was introduced in the chapter *How to write*. If those conclusions are to make sense to a reader, you must order them in a way that makes sense in terms of how you stated the research question. When you have ordered them, flesh them out into a flowing text summarizing the story of your paper.

Incidentally, when you discuss what your results mean, you will sometimes come up with new ideas that are not a direct outcome of your data. It can be hard to present them in an objective way since your experiment was not specifically designed to answer those spinoff questions—your data may simply not be sufficient to draw firm conclusions about them. Most likely, they will require separate experiments with their own control groups and strategies for handling lurking variables and noise. If you want to discuss such ideas, present them as questions for further research. If you don't, your readers may think you draw too far-reaching conclusions from your data and this will detract from your credibility.

The reason why the results and discussion are often merged into one section is that treating the same results in two separate sections tends to become repetitive. Interpreting the results where they first appear also makes it easier for the reader to follow the line of argument. If you merge these sections, make sure that it's clear to the reader what is an objective description of the data and where you make interpretations. As we will see in the next chapter, you can make this difference clearer by describing your results in the past tense and using the present tense when making generalizations from them. If you merge these sections, don't forget to finish it off with a summary of the story of your paper, to drive the message home.

Reading papers, you will have noticed that the IMRaD sections are not the only sections that appear in scientific papers. There are auxiliary parts that you add before and after them, too, and we will look at them now.

Auxiliary parts

The first auxiliary is the *abstract*, which we have touched briefly on already. It's a condensed version of the paper that presents the research question, outlines the investigation, and states the central conclusions in a few hundred words. It has the same function as the back-cover blurb on a novel—it's a summary that's aimed at making people interested in reading the book or, in your case, the paper. It's published along with the title in literature databases to make it easier for researchers to find papers that are relevant to their interests. Everything that I said about the title applies to the abstract as well: it should be concise, to the point, and inspire people to read your paper.

At the end of the paper, there is usually a brief *acknowledgements* section where you thank the organizations that funded your research. This is partly a common courtesy, but it's also important for funding organizations as they sometimes want to track the outcomes of research they have funded. One way to do that is to search for papers that explicitly mention their names. If there are people who contributed to your research but, for one reason or another, did not end up in the author list, this section is a good place to thank them, too.

Finally, at the very end of your paper, you present a list of references to the literature you have cited in the text. There are standards for how to cite and refer to papers and since it's a bit of a messy topic, we will split it off into a separate section.

Citations and references

You cite others to support factual claims and to put your work into the wider context of what's published in the literature. Citations are made in the body of the manuscript. References are listed at the end and uniquely identify the papers you cite, so others can find and read them. But it's not just a matter of listing the papers. As usual, there are rules and conventions to consider.

First of all, there are two main systems for citations. One is called the Vancouver system or, sometimes, the author-number system. The other is called the Harvard system, or the author-date system. In the Vancouver system, citations are numbered consecutively throughout the text. They are usually given within parentheses, square brackets or as superscripts, like this:

References are written within parentheses (1), brackets [1], as superscripts[1], or as a combination of these[1].

When you want to cite two or more authors, you simply add more numbers to the citation:

You can cite two authors [1,2] or as many as you wish [1-5,7,9].

At the end of the manuscript, you list the references in the order they appeared in the text and number them consecutively. A paper citation looks like this:

Hershey AD, Chase M. Independent Functions of Viral Protein and Nucleic Acid in Growth of Bacteriophage. Journal of General Physiology 1952, 36(1):39-56.

The authors' names are followed by the paper title and the name of the journal where it was published. The numbers at the end are the year of publication, the volume with the number of the issue within parentheses, followed by the pages within the issue where the paper was printed.

If your citation refers to a book, you also include the name and location of the publisher:

Millikan RA. The Electron: Its Isolation and Measurement and the Determination of Some of its Properties. Chicago, Il: The University of Chicago Press, 1921.

An advantage of the Vancouver system is that the citations use very little space in the text, making it easy to read the paper with minimal distractions. There is at least one drawback too: If you suddenly need to add new citations in the middle of your manuscript, you have to renumber all the subsequent references. That said, word processors often have software features that handle the numbering and make this less problematic. You may even want to invest in separate referencing software that keeps track of the literature you've read. Through an add-on within your word processor, the software will automatically format your references according to the standard you choose.

The Harvard system mainly differs from the Vancouver system by putting citations within parentheses in the text. Each citation states the author's family name and the year of publication, which is why it's also called the author-date system. In this system, a citation looks like this:

Coffee has been shown to reduce drowsiness (Maxwell et al., 1984).

or

Maxwell et al. (1984) showed that coffee reduces drowsiness.

The sources are then listed alphabetically in the reference list. This is an example of a paper reference:

Maxwell, J., House, G., and Roaster, M., 1984. "Caffeine effects on post-prandial somnolence," Int. J. Beans, 393: 639–40.

Book references are different from paper references in the Harvard system, too:

Maxwell, J., 1984. A Comprehensive Guide to Coffee. New York: Bean Publishing.

One of the advantages of the Harvard system is that since the references are listed alphabetically, new references can be added without having to renumber the others. Another advantage is that readers familiar with your field can identify important references in the text without looking in the reference list. The main disadvantage is that the citations use a lot of space in the text, which can be distracting, especially if you're citing several works in the same sentence.

An important point is that you should avoid mixing the reference systems like this:

The effect was reported by Clark et al. in [1].

Researchers strive to minimize their word count and citing the same work in two different ways constitutes unnecessary verbiage. The only situation where there is reason to cite the name of the author in the Vancouver system is when you cite an important source and you want your readers to instantly realize which one it is.

Of the two main systems, the fields of science, medicine and engineering tend to favor the Vancouver system, or one of its many variants. For example, the American chemical society (ACS), the institute of electrical and electronics engineers (IEEE), the American society of mechanical engineers (ASME), and the American institute of physics (AIP) all have their own versions of the Vancouver style. Fortunately, it's easy to find out which one to use by looking at journals' author-resources pages, or by simply examining the reference lists in their published papers to see how it's done. A quick internet search will also lead you to plenty of sites that describe the styles and give detailed examples of each.

A general advice is to be thorough when you do the proofreading of the references in your manuscript. Many of the details about where to put quotation marks, parentheses around the year of publication, and so on may seem unimportant to you, but errors and mixed styles will make a sloppy impression on editors and reviewers. You want to avoid that.

Now that we covered what goes into the different sections of a paper it's time to delve into how to shape the text itself. In the next chapter we'll talk about what characterizes good scientific text and how those characteristics work at different levels of the text.

Efficiency lesson

What we've discussed in this chapter may seem to have more to do with book-keeping than efficiency but, apart from the truism that a well-structured paper is easy to read, the take-home message is very simple: if you understand the purpose of each part of a paper and pay attention to it, there will be less need for moving things around later, and less effort will be wasted reworking and rewriting what you have already written.

Exercise: Pick out the good paper from your field that you worked with before. Skim it and make notes of the type of content you find in the different sections. How are the contents ordered within each section? What can you learn from how each section is structured?

Exercise: Looking at your notes, do you think all the contents are under the right heading? If not, is there a good reason for it, or would the paper be clearer if the disposition was different?

Exercise: After reading the paper, try to reverse-engineer how the authors chose the title. Which parts of the contents do they draw on in the title and why? Do you think the title attracts all the potential readers that could be interested in reading and citing this paper?

Exercise: Do the same thing with the abstract. From which parts do the authors draw the contents of the abstract? Is this how you would write it?

Exercise: Look at other papers in your field. What citation styles are common? How do citations of journal papers, conference papers, and books differ from each other?

Chapter 7

Shaping your text

If you were an architect designing a house, you probably wouldn't start by choosing the colors on the walls. More likely, you'd begin by finding the best place for the building in relation to access roads and the landscape. You would draw a patio in a sunny spot, for example, and the kitchen close to it. High level decisions like that would come long before details like where to place light switches and kitchen cabinets.

Writing a paper is very similar. You need to decide how your paper should relate to other work long before you decide where to put commas and full stops. Writing is not simply putting words on paper—it's a process taking place on several levels, and we're now moving further down from the overall structure to the work on paragraphs and sentences. Up until now we've gotten by on general principles. From now on we will need to deal with the technicalities of composition. It's time to get acquainted with your writer's toolbox.

The tools of the trade

I'd like to get one common misconception out of the way before we begin. The first few times you try reading scientific papers, they may seem impenetrable and riddled with technical jargon. This is probably the reason why many novice writers think they must use complex language to make their papers look "scientific". Please don't. Good scientific text is not supposed to be complex at all—it should be simple and clear.

This may seem like a paradox. If scientific text is supposed to be simple and clear, why is it sometimes so difficult to read? In all honesty, one reason is that you'll find a lot of bad writing out there, but let's leave that aside. There are more legitimate reasons why scientific papers seem complex. One is that scientists use well-defined, technical concepts when they write. When reading papers, you'll come across terms like *state-space*, *phenotype*, *scalar dissipation rate*, or (one of my personal favorites) *postprandial somnolence* (also known as food coma). To outsiders, a text with terms like these reads as if it were written in some secret language, but to insiders—which is the target group of a scientific paper—they are a help in understanding exactly what the author is referring to. Such terms aren't used to make the text complex. They're used because they carry exact meanings. In fact, your text would become hopelessly complex if you had to *replace* those terms with exact explanations of what they mean. Try to write about a carpark without using the word carpark, for example, and you'll see what I mean. Well-defined concepts are necessary for efficient communication.

Another reason why scientific text can be difficult to read is that it's designed to be concise. All accomplished writers work hard to remove words that don't do any useful work in the text, but researchers go further than that. They even limit the number of printed characters by using acronyms, abbreviations and variable names in the body of the text. As you get used to reading scientific papers, you'll realize that this often improves the readability. Rather than spelling out a term like *Sauter mean diameter* twenty times in a paper, scientists substitute it with SMD to make sentences shorter. On the other hand, this means that novice readers often have to read slowly before they get used to the compact style. Inch by inch, the columns of a scientific journal contain more information than a newspaper article.

Both these points are related to scientific style, which is one of two important tools in your toolbox. Style is about writing in precise and concise scientific language, delivering your message in the voice of a professional researcher. But style will get you nowhere if you don't know how to structure your text in a way that's compatible with how readers take in and process information. This is your other main tool, and I will call it function. Let's start with that, since it's fundamental to all writing.

Function—making the text work

I once made a survey about scientific writing among the twenty-or-so PhD students in the research group where I work. I wasn't too surprised to find that almost all of them thought writing papers was pretty difficult. When they explained why it was difficult, they described problems with writing text that flowed nicely, expressing the scientific question clearly, describing results in a compelling way, and establishing a logical path through the text. Though none of these students were native English speakers, there were almost no comments about difficulties with spelling and grammar—most saw shaping a readable text as the main challenge of writing. In other words, almost all of their problems had to do with the function of the text.

You recognize a well-functioning text by the fact that it's easy to follow. When it isn't, there are generally two problem areas to look into. The first has to do with the disposition; how you organize the contents into sections and subsections. The other is the structure of the text, or how you line up individual paragraphs, sentences and words. If you have problems with this, it could be because sentences are not sufficiently linked with each other to make sense, or because words are combined in ways that defy interpretation. The latter goes back to the correct use of English. It goes without saying that what you write must follow the established rules of composition, since those rules are there to make sure your sentences make sense. I won't go further into that, as there are whole books on the topic that explain the rules much better than I could. Here, I'll focus on how you organize the text in sections, subsections and paragraphs.

Shaping a text that works starts with the housekeeping we talked about in the last chapter: putting everything under the heading where it belongs. The next step is to focus your writing. Just as one paper should focus on one research question, each section in the paper should deal with one topic (yes, the ones we talked about in the previous chapter), and if you use subsections, let them cover one subtopic each. At the next level down, one paragraph should describe one idea, and each sentence should convey no more than one thought. Focusing your writing like this is crucial if your readers are to understand what you write. Clarity is not only about the information you present—mostly, it's about how you structure it. With the three-step drafting process I described in Chapter 3, an ordered structure will grow naturally from the strawman draft since each bullet under a heading will be the basis of a paragraph in the final paper. If you don't use that method, you will have to think more consciously about the disposition, and probably spend more time with revision before you're satisfied.

When the information is in the right sections and paragraphs, it's time to connect the dots—to create a flow that step by step ties the research question at the beginning of your paper to the conclusions at the end. Each part of the text is a link in that chain, and the links stick together by different sorts of text transitions—words and phrases that connect paragraphs, sentences and even parts of sentences. If you don't connect them your text will read like a disjointed series of statements, like in the following example, which describes a field experiment involving birds:

> *Capture and manipulation might influence subsequent behavior. This could confound interpretation. Flight displays and territorial disputes were counted in each male before and after the treatment.*

Many novice writers tend to stack short sentences like these upon each other, maybe because they think short sentences make a text easier to read. In reality, your text flows better if you mix short sentences with longer ones. Since all these sentences describe the same thought, binding them together makes the message much clearer:

> *As capture and manipulation might influence subsequent behavior, which could confound interpretation, flight displays and territorial disputes were counted in each male before and after the treatment.*

Adding the word "as" and replacing a couple of full stops with commas turned the separate statements into something that almost resembles a short story. Sometimes, binding is as easy as this, or as adding the little word "and" between clauses that belong together, but there are other types of transitions as well. For example, when a sentence adds information to the previous one, you could start it with a transition like "for example" (duh), "in addition to this", "moreover", or maybe "similarly". If the next sentence supports the previous, you might begin it with a phrase like "in fact", "surely", or "in other words"; if it opposes the previous sentence, you might choose "on the other hand", "however", "in reality", or something similar. Texts that work well are full of transitions like these. Take a moment to read the following excerpt from a paper on chimpanzee behavior (where I have removed the citations for convenience) and look for the transitions:

[…] Many nonhuman animals demonstrate cooperative abilities, and recent empirical studies have also revealed that some nonhuman primates can help or share food with conspecifics without any direct benefit to themselves. However, our understanding of the cognitive mechanisms involved remains limited and urgently requires further investigation, especially from a comparative perspective.

Regarding the cognitive mechanisms involved in helping, much focus has been given to "targeted helping", which is defined as help and care based on the cognitive appreciation of the need or situation of others. [...][14]

How many did you spot? That's right. Every clause starts with a transition word (and, however, especially, regarding, which). You wouldn't think that there was anything special about these words if you didn't look for transitions, just like you wouldn't remark on the nuts and bolts that hold a machine together if you weren't interested in taking it apart. Text binding also works at the higher level of paragraphs. If you read the passage again, you will notice that the whole first clause of the second paragraph is a transition phrase, since it picks up a sub-topic of the previous paragraph and specifies that the following paragraph will be about that sub-topic in particular.

Incidentally, your teachers might have told you at an early age never to start a sentence with words like *and* or *but*. But as Steven Pinker explains, they probably do this because children "sometimes write in fragments. And are shaky about when to use periods. And when to capitalize." [1] Once you have mastered these basics, it's better to forget what your teacher told you. In fact, *and*, *but*, and *so* are some of the commonest text binders, typically used to avoid monstrously long sentences. Following the example of distinguished writers, you may use them whenever you see fit.

Another useful tool for creating structure through transitions is what is sometimes called the *tell-tell-tell* technique. Tell-tell-tell is shorthand for a set of three instructions:

1. First, tell them what you're going to tell them.
2. Then tell them.
3. Finally, tell them what you told them.

This probably sounds odd the first time you hear it, but the method is both simple and useful. When you tell your readers what you're going to tell them, you make them aware that a new part of the text is coming up. When you tell them what you told them, you're summarizing a part to drive the message home before you move on. You'll get a flavor of how it works in the following excerpt, adopted from a paper about diesel engines:

> *An additional distinct feature of this study is the use of a new fuel tracer technique. This technique, which employs 1-methylnaphthalene as a tracer in a mixture of the diesel primary reference fuels, allows closer matching of the physical properties of the surrogate fuel mixture to those of standard diesel fuel. In particular, the fuel volatility and density, properties which affect the fuel jet vaporization and air entrainment, are more closely matched than in a blend of toluene, n-heptane, and isooctane. This technique clearly improves our ability to quantitatively measure in-cylinder fuel-air ratio distributions in diesel engines.*[15]

Even if you don't fully understand the technical details of this passage, you can probably see the structure. The first sentence mentions "another distinct feature" of the study. It guides the reader towards a new idea that's about to be explained—the authors tell us what they're going to tell us. The last sentence wraps the idea up by briefly summarizing how the idea is an improvement—they tell us what they told us. Incidentally, if you think about it, the very form of a scientific paper employs the tell-tell-tell technique by putting an abstract at the beginning, describing what the author is going to tell you, and summarizing the conclusions at the end, describing what he has told you.

It's important not to use tell-tell-tell too heavy-handedly, though. If you start a passage by saying "I am now going to explain…" and finish it by "In this passage I have explained…", the tool becomes intrusive—it pulls the readers' attention from what you're saying to how you're saying it. The only situation when that type of obvious metacommunication is helpful is in oral presentations, where you can't use headings and paragraphs to create structure.

If you recall the survey I mentioned at the beginning of this section, you may wonder how all this connects with what the students said there: how difficult it was to write a text that flows nicely, to express the scientific question clearly, to describe results in a compelling way, and to establish a logical path through the text. Well, I hope to have shown that text transitions are the very tools you need to accomplish these things. What seemed to be the major obstacle for most of these PhD students really comes down to something relatively easy. But it's easy in theory. As with any other skill, you have to experiment, evaluate, and experiment again before you get the hang of using text transitions. And just as there can be a lack of binding in a text, it's possible to overdo it. You probably have a problem with too long sentences if readers complain about having to read a passage several times to understand what it means. This could be a symptom that you have squeezed more than one thought into each sentence, or more than one idea into each paragraph. The trick is to bind the text together and focus your writing at the same time.

Style

If you read a scientific paper, a newspaper, and a user manual, you will get distinctly different impressions of the texts, because they're written in distinctly different styles. Style is not a question of good or bad. It's rather something that tells the reader what type of text she's reading. The reason why we care about style at all is that your text communicates about more than your data and your research—it also communicates something about you as a researcher. It tells readers that you know your subject and have a professional attitude to it. This is important. If you don't take what you write seriously, nobody else will either.

There are three basic features that help you write something that reads as scientific text: it's written in a *formal language* and there's an aspiration for *objectivity* and *economy* in what you write. The most important means to cultivate your serious image is the formal language. Take a look at the following list of words:

- Dispute
- Debate
- Discuss

- Speak
- Talk
- Chat
- Yap

You could use any of them to describe the same thing, but I think you'll agree that some are more likely to turn up in official situations while others hardly are heard outside private conversations. If you're writing a paper and find yourself choosing from a range of words like this, you should pick words at the official end of the spectrum and save the informal ones for when you are talking about your work over coffee at the office. (Incidentally, this means that you shouldn't use this book as a style model for your papers—I'm intentionally writing in a more informal voice than the average scientific writer, in the hope that it will make the book at least slightly more pleasant to read than the average scientific paper.)

If you were talking about your work with a colleague, it might sound something like this:

I have tried to draw a picture of how birds control their blood sugar in all kinds of cool ways, but there's still a lot we don't know.

If you ask me, this sentence is easy to understand and does a good job of giving us the important information—not a bad text at all if you're just looking at the function. But when I picked the passage from a scientific journal it read like this:

This review has attempted to elucidate many of the fascinating attributes of avian glucose regulation. However, there is still much to be learned.

This obviously has a different style, but I wouldn't say that it's obviously *better*. Although it uses slightly fewer words, the words are longer on average. I wouldn't say it's worse, either: the term "glucose regulation" is more precise than "controlling their blood sugar", for example. The main difference is that the last version uses scientific terms and a more formal language. The point is this: when we read it, we tend to think of the writer as a pro—someone who takes his job seriously and pays much closer attention to his writing than to ordering pizza on Saturday night. That's what scientific style helps you achieve.

You could say that style is the writer's equivalent of coming dressed for the occasion. Just as you wouldn't show up at the Nobel prize banquet in a t-shirt and sneakers, you wouldn't wear an evening gown to a baseball game—not because one of these is a better way of dressing, but simply because you use them in different situations. When writing a paper, you use scientific style to show readers that you understand the context you're writing in.

One of the hurdles to overcome when learning to write in a professional voice is that many of us develop our sense of English through popular culture. This is especially true for non-native speakers, who often don't hear spoken English on a day-to-day basis. Every so often, phrases we pick up from movies and other popular media pop up in our writing. For example,

Another great thing about the technique is that it's non-intrusive.

isn't difficult to understand, but the word "great" seems out of place in scientific text. Revising it to:

Non-intrusiveness is another important feature of the technique.

not only gives the text a more professional impression, it actually says the same thing in fewer words. Here's another example of colloquial language in scientific text:

The spectra of large molecules have a lot of peaks.

If this sentence is revised to:

Large molecules have complex spectra.

we express the same thing in a more professional voice using only half the number of words.

Although you must learn to use formal language to write a good scientific paper, don't fall into the trap of overdoing it. It's all too common (sadly, even among seasoned researchers) to get carried away with abstract terms and complex sentence structures, often to the point of writing complete gibberish. Apart from being confusing, this often gives a pretentious and comical impression. There's a classic

Calvin & Hobbes strip that illustrates this nicely, as six-year-old Calvin shows his pet tiger the title of his book report for school:

> *"The dynamics of interbeing and monological imperatives in Dick and Jane: a study in psychic transrelational gender modes"*

"With a little practice," Calvin remarks, "writing can be an intimidating and impenetrable fog—academia, here I come!"

So, exactly how much formality and scientific lingo is too much then? That's, as they say, a good question. It's useful to think of writing as cooking. Adding a pinch of salt brings out the flavors of a soup that would otherwise be bland and uninteresting. Adding too much, on the other hand, will make it completely inedible. Scientific style works exactly like that. As you gradually move from informal to formal writing, you first straighten the text up, bringing out its precision and clarity. But if you move too far, your text grows into Calvin's intimidating and impenetrable fog. The simple answer to the question is that the proof of the text is in the reading. If style gets in the way of understanding, you're clearly overdoing it.

The second feature of scientific style was *objectivity*. Scientists pride themselves with basing their conclusions on hard evidence, not mere opinions, and this means that when you make assumptions in your text, you are expected to explain that they *are* assumptions. When you make factual statements, you are expected to support them with evidence—either in your own data or by reference to other work. Even when you're stating an obvious truth you will do well to back it up with a logical argument, or at least state that your claim is widely accepted. The truth may not be obvious to all your readers.

Objectivity also works on a subtler level that, for lack of a better word, I'm going to call rhetoric. I fully understand if you wince at seeing this word in the same sentence as objectivity, especially if you've seen politicians pull rhetorical tricks on each other in debates. It's true that rhetoric can be used to make arguments seem better than they really are, but that's not what I'm after here. To scientists, rhetoric is simply a tool for making their arguments clear. If you aren't aware of the rhetoric dimension of your text, it could prompt unnecessary misinterpretations.

Say that you're writing about sources of measurement error in your experiment. If you just tell your readers that the signal-to-noise ratio was lower than you had hoped for, you could bring on unnecessary criticism or even make them lose interest in your paper. In fact, your contribution may be all the more important if you were able to get useful data under challenging conditions. If you did, you should make that clear to your readers. Objectivity involves putting challenges into perspective and explaining how you overcame them. This is a rhetorical move.

If overemphasizing weaknesses in your work is a problem, overemphasizing strengths is just as problematic. This is the reason why academic text contains so much cautious language. You have probably seen it many times: instead of stating that their findings prove an idea, researchers will write that the data *support* an hypothesis; or a strong trend in the data may be described as *suggesting* a certain interpretation rather than proving a fact. The obvious reason is that there are often several ways to interpret data patterns. Your readers know this, and you must show them that you know it too. Modifying the strength of claims like this is called *hedging*, perhaps because it's used to mark the limitations of your conclusions, much like a hedge marks the boundaries of a garden. Like any technique, hedging should be used with judgement. Too little will make it look like you're blowing your results out of proportion, while too much will give the impression that you don't trust your data. You should use hedging to increase your readers' confidence in what you're telling them, not the other way around. Rhetoric in science writing, then, is not a way to cover up poor arguments, but a way to convey a fair picture of the truth.

Another point related to objectivity is that scientists tend to avoid the first-person pronouns *I* and *we* in their writing. This goes back to an old fear of coming across as partial or subjective. Writing in the third person ("the authors found") instead of the first ("we found") is a way of emphasizing the action rather than the agent and this at least gives an *impression* of objectivity. The drawback of writing in the third person is that it forces us to use verbose sentences, as in this example:

The technique was chosen by the authors because it is non-intrusive.

Written in the third person, this sentence emphasizes the technique rather than the authors, but it also shows how easy it is to fall into the trap of using the passive voice when writing in the third person. Writing in the first person and using the active voice, the sentence changes to:

We chose the technique because it is non-intrusive.

This is both shorter and easier to understand since it gives a clearer sense of what's going on.

The tradition of writing about yourself in the third person is, quite frankly, silly. It stems from an era when scientists strived to get to what they thought were absolute truths by scrutinizing what they thought were absolute facts in an almost mechanical manner. In those days, assumptions and interpretations weren't accepted as parts of good research. The problem is, when we look at the history of science, it's obvious that assumptions and interpretations have always been at the heart of the process. Scientists are not machines—they are intelligent observers who strive to understand the world through the creative process we call research. In my opinion, pretending otherwise verges on dishonesty. You should address objectivity by openly discussing your assumptions and interpretations, not by pretending you weren't there when the research was done.

Today, some journals allow you to write in the first person, but there are still many that don't. If the demand isn't explicit, I propose that you try the first-person perspective. If your editor comments on it, try to explain that you made a conscious choice to make the text concise, direct and clear. But if your editor still insists that you switch to the third person, I would give in—after all, it's difficult to teach old dogs new tricks.

The final characteristic of good scientific writing is the strive for *economy*. Scientists try hard to express themselves in as few words and even as few characters as possible. This is the reason why you frequently come across abbreviations and acronyms in scientific papers—something that's almost unique for scientific text, since it's considered bad form in most other types of writing.

You have probably noticed that the scientific literature is full of abbreviations like *et al.*, *i.e.* and *e.g.* When reading the text aloud, abbreviations are pronounced as words. *Et al.* reads "and others" (or *et alia* if you like to speak latin). *I.e.* reads "that is" (*id est*) and *e.g.* reads "for example" (*exempli gratia*). While abbreviations are any shortened versions of words, acronyms are formed from the initial letters of a combination of words and written in capitals. DNA, for example, is both written and pronounced as a sequence of three letters, simply because deoxyribonucleic acid is such a jawbreaker of a word. LIF and IMEP are other examples of useful acronyms, sparing us the trouble of having to stumble our way through terms like laser-induced fluorescence and indicated mean effective pressure in every other paragraph of a paper. Some acronyms are pronounced as words, simply because they look like words. A common example is ANOVA (analysis of variance). Another example is LASER (light amplification by stimulated emission of radiation), which has become so established that people now tend to write it in lower case letters, like any other word. Purists would say that these are the real acronyms, since the ones that cannot be pronounced as words technically are called initialisms, but most people don't make a distinction.

As a general rule, if long sequences of words like these show up repeatedly in your manuscript, you're expected to either use an existing acronym or invent a new one. Introduce it within parentheses the first time it appears in the text, like this:

A three-letter acronym (TLA) is pronounced as a sequence of three letters.

Note that I didn't capitalize the words that the acronym is formed from. (In English, capitals are reserved for special situations, like beginnings of sentences and proper names—and your readers are smart enough to figure out how the acronym is formed anyway.) The next time you need the phrase, you simply use the acronym:

We have discussed DNA, LIF and other TLAs.

Apart from using abbreviations and acronyms, the key to writing economically is to avoid clutter and redundancy. You should always strive to formulate your text as directly and concisely as possible. No matter how hard you try to do that, however, you will find that some passages are longer and more complex than they need to be when you review your work, and you will often find that you are repeating yourself. In other words, you usually need to revise your text several times to end up with something that's as concise and clear as you would expect a published paper to be. I'll return to this in Chapter 9, which deals with revision. But before we get to that, the next chapter will expand a little on the function of the text. I'll discuss an important tool for making your text compatible with how your readers' brains take in a written message, which is to tell it like a story.

Efficiency lesson

When you shape your text, begin with the housekeeping: put all the contents under the headings and subheadings where they belong. Then focus the text to make every section deal with one topic, every paragraph with one idea, and every sentence with one thought. When you have attended to these basics, link the text together with transitions and enhance the flow by preparing the reader for what's waiting ahead. As you learn to use these tools, you will enhance the readability of what you write. This avoids wasted time and wasted work by reducing the need for revision in the next step. Once you have ensured the function of the text, polish the details to the adequate level of precision and formality, adding the elements of scientific style.

Exercise: Read a good paper with the idea of focused writing in mind. Is there one idea per paragraph, one thought per sentence? Make a strawman outline of the paper and list the ideas covered by each paragraph as bullets. Do you now see how you should shape the bullets of your own strawman?

Exercise: Go through the paper and mark all the transition words in the sentences and transition clauses between paragraphs—you'll be surprised at how many there are, and that they were there all along without you noticing them before. Do you see how they enhance the readability?

Exercise: Take a bullet or two from the strawman outline you made above and write a paragraph from them in your own words. Then compare the result with the published paper. Are there large

differences in style? How could you improve the style in your version?
Can you transfer these insights to your own writing?

70

Chapter 8

Storytelling for scientists

A wise friend of mine says that he always asks himself the same question when he gets a draft that doesn't quite seem to work: Are they telling me a story? What he means is that a paper must be *about* something if we are to bother ourselves with reading it. I have asked myself the same question over the years and discovered that the story element goes even deeper than that. Stories have a structure of their own—a structure that feeds directly into how we understand the world around us. This means that we can make it easier for readers to take our message in by using elements of storytelling in our papers. Sounds vague? Let me explain.

The power of stories

Take a few seconds to look at the following few numbers:

5 7 0 4 2 7 3 8 4 9

Now, close your eyes and try to repeat them.

How did it go? My guess is that you got a part of the sequence right, probably at the beginning of the line, but few people manage to memorize the whole series.

Now close your eyes and try to retell the storyline of Jurassic Park.

Most people find this much easier. But how can it be easier to remember the story of a movie that we haven't seen in years than to repeat a series of ten numbers that we took a good look at just a few seconds ago? After all, the amount of information contained in the story is much greater than that in the numbers. The reason seems to be that our brains have a natural talent for relating to stories. In fact, stories seem to be how we interpret the world.

When you do something as simple as crossing the street, a stream of impressions flow over you. Your eyes see traffic lights, trees, and cars moving in different directions. Your ears take in the sounds of engines, birds singing, and rolling tires. If you weren't able to organize these separate impressions into patterns and sort them into what's relevant and what's not, there's a risk that you wouldn't make it across the street alive. Subconsciously, you connect these impressions and interpret them as a causal flow of events. You make predictions about what's going to happen next, so you can act in a meaningful way when it is safe to do so. Turning impressions into rudimentary stories is how our brains extract meaning from the chaos around us.

Apart from being the basis of our experience in this way, stories are also an efficient way to pass our knowledge on to others. If you read about a poisonous snake in an encyclopedia, you will get to know it through facts and figures. If somebody told you about an encounter with the same snake in the wild, on the other hand, your impression would be much more vivid. When they tell you the story of how they almost stepped on the creature, how it reacted and what they did to get away, you will almost feel as if you were there yourself. If one day you come across a snake like that, you will probably find the story much more useful than the entry in the encyclopedia, because it has become part of your experience in a way that facts and figures never do. Stories turn other's experiences into your own.

Some have proposed that there are biological reasons why we experience stories so vividly. Without stories, we would only be able to learn from our own mistakes—mistakes that could be deadly, especially if you step on a snake. Perhaps those of our ancestors who had a talent for relating to stories were more likely to survive encounters with snakes and other dangerous situations, because they had the ability to learn from others' experience? If their ability were passed down with the genes, our knack for stories may be what biologists call an adaptation.[16] It may be hard-coded into our DNA.

But what do stories have to do with scientific writing? And do they have anything to do with writing efficiently?

Have you ever wondered why most people prefer reading novels to reading textbooks? The only reason I can find for experiencing those types of text so differently is that novels tell stories and most textbooks don't. Our brains are wired to look for agents, intentions and purpose.[17] Stories make this easy for us, since they have those elements built into them in a way that most technical texts don't. Although a scientific paper will never be as accessible as a work of fiction, that doesn't mean there aren't tools and tricks in the storyteller's toolshed that can help you make your papers more compelling. In this chapter I hope to convince you that building a storyline into your paper will reduce the amount of revision needed to make it readable to an outsider. In other words, I hope to convince you that storytelling can make your writing better and more efficient at the same time.

What is a story?

A story has a sense of action, something that drives it forward. Take a look at the following few lines:

'Twas brillig, and the slithy toves
  Did gyre and gimble in the wabe;
All mimsy were the borogoves,
  And the mome raths outgrabe.

'Beware the Jabberwock, my son!
  The jaws that bite, the claws that catch!
Beware the Jubjub bird, and shun
  The frumious Bandersnatch!' [18]

You're right, these are the opening lines of the poem Jabberwocky by Lewis Carroll. Although almost every second word in this verse is made-up nonsense, it has a sense of story. Even though I don't know what a borogove is, or what it means to be mimsy, I still get a distinct feeling that something important is about to happen. This entices me to read on.

Many scientific texts, although they consist exclusively of well-defined words, don't manage to give us a sense of anything at all. This is the difference between stories and other types of writing. A story isn't static—it creates an anticipation about something that's about to happen. That anticipation is what pulls us along with the story. Creating a story isn't a question of style—you build that anticipation by *structuring* your text to create a sense of forward motion. If you can learn to do that, it will help you pull your readers from your research problem all the way to your conclusions without losing them on the way.

At the most basic level, a story takes place between a before and an after. In the beginning we meet the story characters and see them going about their ordinary lives—their "before". Then the story happens. The characters are pulled from their everyday lives and thrown into a crisis of some sort. They struggle to overcome the problems and eventually manage to go back to their lives again, but those lives have now changed as a result of what happened in the story—they have entered their "after".

As nice as ordinary life may be for the characters, it's not particularly interesting for us as an audience. We don't want to see characters drinking coffee, washing up, and getting along—we want to see them dealing with crises and hardship. We want a good story, and that begins when their ordinary life is disturbed by an external event.

I'll digress with a couple of examples from Jurassic Park before we move on, just to make sure you understand how the story elements work. At the beginning of the movie, we meet paleontologists Alan Grant and Ellie Sattler as they dig out the fossil of a velociraptor at an excavation site. This is what they do in their ordinary lives, their "before". The disturbance occurs when Mike Hammond, the wealthy entrepreneur that funds their research, interrupts the dig and persuades them to join him on the far-off island Isla Nubar. Arriving there, they are astonished to find that it's inhabited by live dinosaurs. They can't believe their eyes. This is the change in their lives that sets the story wheel rolling.

Now for the crises and hardship. Once we get to the island, the movie takes us through a sequence of scenes that illustrate the main conflict of the story and how the characters gradually overcome it. Grant is worried when he realizes that Hammond is turning the island into a theme park, planning to bring tourists in to watch the prehistoric beasts. He fears for the safety of the visitors and this turns out to be justified when, suddenly, the beasts are on the loose. The story question poses itself: Will they make it from the island alive? This is the question that keeps us engaged in the story until the very end.

In one of the most intense scenes, a T-Rex demolishes a car with the Hammond's terrified grandchildren inside it. The level of conflict escalates even further when the park's velociraptors manage to escape. Towards the end of the story, Grant, Sattler, and the children reach the park's abandoned control center and find themselves chased by velociraptors through the complex. At the height of the conflict they are cornered and all hope seems lost. Then the T-Rex comes crashing into the building, attacking the raptors and buying our protagonists just enough time to escape the island. At the climax of the movie, they leave by helicopter as the T-Rex gives a roar of victory to illustrate the theme of the story: man is an arrogant fool to tamper with Mother Nature's order—she is far too powerful, and we are never as smart as we think.

At this point, there is no doubt in our minds that we have reached the end of the story. We have seen the protagonists escape from the island and transition into their "after". They go back to their lives, but those lives are not quite what they were before the story began. The story has left marks—our protagonists emerge wiser than they came in.

So, a story takes place between a before and an after. Between these points, the story is built from the basic building blocks of *conflict*, *action* and *change*. Conflict comes first. It's created when something keeps a character from reaching her goal. It doesn't have to be a conflict between two persons. In story language, a conflict is any obstacle standing in the protagonist's way. In Jurassic Park, all things that add to making it difficult for our protagonists to escape the island alive are conflicts. To overcome them, the characters must take *action*. The action, in turn, creates a *change* in the story, from one situation to the next. As shown in the figure below, this change often leads to a new conflict that sets the story wheel spinning one more turn.

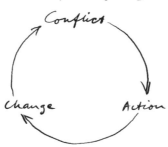

The car scene in Jurassic Park, for example, takes place on a bridge where a T-Rex is trying to eat the two children trapped inside the car. This is the *conflict* of the scene. Grant then takes *action*, waving a flare and throwing it off the bridge. The flare distracts the animal long enough for Grant to descend with the girl from the bridge using a rope. This is the *change*; they are temporarily off the hook. But the change leads to a new conflict: the T-Rex pushes the car off the bridge and Grant and the girl, who are below it, have to take action not to be hit by the car. The change and the next conflict arise when the car is stuck in a tree beneath the bridge with the boy still inside. And so it continues. This is an example of how the story wheel spins over and over, from conflict via action to change, until the main conflict is solved and the story has come to its conclusion.

You may think this formula seems too simple to work, but its simplicity is probably the reason why it can be varied indefinitely. I could have picked almost any story in the world, from a Shakespeare drama to a superhero comic, and we would find that they all follow the same structure. They do because it's a format we instinctively relate to. When we see a character in trouble, we empathize with her and understand why she acts like she does. We experience the story world through her eyes, feel what she feels and learn what she learns.

Story in scientific text

Writing scientific text is obviously very different from writing fiction. The most important difference is perhaps that research papers don't have characters in them. Although everybody understands that research is a series of actions carried out by *people* to overcome a conflict in the form of an unresolved scientific problem, the researchers are often suspiciously absent from the text. At best, they will refer to themselves in the anonymous third person. They may write that *the authors* assumed this, *the authors* concluded that, but they try very hard indeed to sweep their texts clean of any trace of a living, breathing, thinking person. This is one of the reasons why it's more difficult for us to relate to scientific text than to stories, but there's not much we can do about that—those are the rules of the game we're playing.

But although papers don't have explicit story characters, the protagonist is always implicit in the researcher or team that made the study, and Mother Nature can often be seen as an implicit antagonist. She puts obstacles in the researchers' way to keep them from unraveling her secrets. We don't explicitly write about research as a struggle between protagonist and antagonist, of course, but if you keep this picture at the back of your mind, it will be easier to find the useful story elements of your text. To make the overall conflict clear, your paper must have a goal—something that gives us a sense of direction through the text. You must make the reader understand which question you are trying to answer and why it is important. And just as a fiction writer, you can pull readers along in your text by using conflict, action and change. There's an inherent dramatic structure in research that you should make use of. Researchers set out to reach goals, they meet with obstacles on the way and have to take action to overcome them. It could be that you have to find a measurement technique that's suited for a challenging environment, or you may choose a particular statistical method to handle problems with noise in your data. Each investigation is unique because it answers a unique question by solving unique problems, and you should tell your readers about those problems. Never introduce a measurement technique without first explaining why it's suited to your situation. Before you describe the details of your analysis method, explain the problem it's meant to solve. In other words, describe every action in your experiment as a response to a conflict. If your readers don't understand that the solution to each little problem in your paper is necessary for attaining the overall goal, they may fail to understand why you're writing about it in the first place.

Let's look at a couple of examples to see how conflict can be used in scientific text. The following excerpt (used with permission) comes from the introduction of an early draft about an engine experiment:

In direct-injection engines, the turbulence generated by bulk flow structures and the fuel injection enhances small-scale mixing in the cylinder. Injection strategies and combustion chamber geometries thereby affect the ignition delay through their effects on the turbulence. In this work, cycle-resolved high-speed particle imaging velocimetry (PIV) was employed to aid the understanding of how the injection strategy affects mixture preparation in an optically accessible engine. It is previously known that combustion characteristics change when using single, double, and triple injections, but it is not well known how it affects the turbulence level. In this paper, the differences between injection strategies and their effects on the in-cylinder flow and fuel-air mixing will be investigated.

Even though some of the technical terms may be unfamiliar, it's not difficult to see that this text seems vague. The passage is meant to motivate the whole experiment, but we don't get a clear sense of what we can expect to learn from it. It says that we don't know how the injection strategy affects the turbulence level, but it only gives vague hints as to why it would be interesting to know something about it. It explains that we can expect to find comparisons between injection strategies in the paper, but not why we should be interested. In short, there is no story question.

If you read the opening chapters of a novel without getting a glimpse of the central conflict of the story, you would put it aside and pick up another book. If you don't understand what the characters' struggle is about, everything they do will seem like random actions. The same goes for a scientific paper, or any other text for that matter. We want to get a clear sense of what the paper is about and why it's important. Storytellers show this through conflict, and that's exactly what the excerpt above lacks.

The following paragraph comes from the introduction to a paper describing a behavioral experiment on chimpanzees. Again, there are a few concepts and technical terms in the text that could make it difficult to understand the details, but it's the structure of the text that we are interested in here:

Why do chimpanzees seldom help others without being requested? One plausible explanation from the perspective of cognitive mechanisms is that chimpanzees cannot understand another's goal upon witnessing another's predicament. Many still believe that humans are unique in this respect because we are the only animal species endowed with unique "theory of mind" abilities enabling us to understand the goals and to share the intentions of others. [...] Nevertheless, we still know little about the cognitive mechanisms underlying helping behavior in nonhuman animals, and no study has empirically examined if and how chimpanzees understand others' goals in these types of helping contexts. [For this reason] we developed an experimental paradigm aimed at examining chimpanzees' ability and flexibility in effectively helping a conspecific depending on his/her specific needs.[14]

This text has a much clearer direction, and one reason for this is that it starts by raising a question. How can it be that chimps don't offer help to each other unless they are asked for it? This is the central question of the paper; the research problem that represents the central conflict faced by the researchers. The text also establishes a knowledge gap that must be bridged to resolve the conflict. I left out a discussion about previous research for brevity, but it is summed up in the statement that despite the previous work, we still don't know much about the chimps' behavior. This helps us understand that the question is not an easy one to answer. When the authors present the action taken in response to this conflict—the development of a new experimental paradigm—we immediately understand why they did it. Even if we don't know the first thing about chimpanzee behavior, we cannot help but get a little interested in finding out if they will succeed. We are hooked by the story.

Both these passages are taken from introduction sections and aim to define the central research questions of the papers where they appear. As we have seen, using conflict makes this much more effective. But conflict can also be used at lower text levels. The following two sentences are cut from papers that deal with the morphology of birds. Here is the first one:

> *The bivariate relationships were explored with linear regressions, and tested with analyses of variance and Spearman rank correlations.*

This formulation is typical for scientific text and could come from a paper in any field. We get a straight description of what was done without further motivation. Compare it to the following sentence:

> *To avoid bias, I searched each territory in proportion to its area of nesting habitat (tall, rank grass).*

This sentence has quite a different feeling, and it's not only because it is written in the first person. It starts with a conflict, a risk of bias that should be avoided. It then continues with an action in response to the conflict. It even includes a bit of the setting within parentheses. Of course, the description of the territory is scientifically relevant and not something that was added just to spice the text up, but did you notice how this snippet of information almost transported you to the site?

Couldn't you almost feel that tall, rank grass brushing against your legs as you searched the territory in proportion to its area of nesting habitat?

Just as fiction writers don't use conflict in every sentence of their novels, you shouldn't strive to use it in every sentence of your paper. I just gave these illustrative examples to show how conflict increases our interest in a text. The important point I am trying to make is that when you show your readers a conflict, the action that follows immediately becomes interesting. An action without conflict, on the other hand, is just information. It may serve a purpose, but if it isn't motivated by conflict the reader has to work harder to understand what that purpose is.

Acts and scenes

So, a story is a sequence of events that transports the reader from a before towards an after. In a work of fiction, these events are usually delivered in three packages to create what is called a dramatic arc. I am talking about the classic three-act structure.

The dramatic arc describes how the conflict rises to a peak before it drops again at the end. Each act has its own role in creating this arc. Act I presents the characters and the story problem they need to solve. Act II develops the main story in a sequence of scenes built from the elements of conflict, action and change. The action rises until, finally, Act III presents the resolution. And, believe it or not, scientific papers actually have a similar structure.

First, there is a part that presents the research problem. This is the introduction (Act I). In the next part, the team of researchers struggle with solving the problem by designing an experiment, taking precautions to handle background factors and noise, and gathering data (Act II). Finally, there is a resolution where the results are put into context, conclusions are drawn and the problem is solved (Act III). Just like a story, your investigation takes place between a before and an after. It begins with a disturbance of the status quo; perhaps an unexpected observation, the identification of a gap in our knowledge, or whatever makes you formulate your research question in the first place. It then continues as a series of actions. You are constantly handling conflict in a scientific investigation, working to overcome obstacles that stand between you and your goal. Finally, you transition into the after. This is a place where you emerge wiser than you came in—where the question that started your investigation has been answered and our knowledge has changed as a result of your investigation.

The three-act format is the highest level of structure in a story. At the level below it, fictional stories are structured into scenes with individual scene goals. An example from Jurassic park is the car scene I mentioned before, where Grant finally succeeds with the scene goal of escaping from the T-Rex with the children. Although a scientific text doesn't have scenes with setting, characters and dialogue, it's still important to spur the reader's interest at each step along the way by adding this finer structure to your text. When you describe the actions that make up your investigation, your readers want to know the purposes of those actions. The tell-tell-tell technique introduced in the previous chapter is one potential model for structuring a paper into rudimentary scenes. Think of it as first telling your readers about the conflict at a particular stage of your investigation, for example explaining why you had to deal with a particular source of noise. Then tell them which actions you took to overcome the obstacle, perhaps by adding a feature to your experimental setup or using a certain analysis technique. Finally, you tell them how the situation changed as a result of your actions.

Find your own way

The concept of storytelling seems to pop up in many fields these days, but thinking of scientific text in terms of stories is definitely unfamiliar to most researchers. This means that you can't expect your academic advisors to teach you how to do it. My recommendation is that you experiment with the story perspective on your own to find ways to increase the readability of your texts. You could begin by trying to understand what defines the before and after of your investigation. This is crucial, because it defines your scientific contribution. Then brainstorm with yourself about what makes up the three-act structure of your paper. Can you build a rudimentary dramatic arc? Try to understand which "scenes" should go into which acts and what the goals of those scenes are. In each scene, make sure your readers understand the conflict before you show them the action. Experiment with these concepts in ways that suit the scientific context. When it comes to writing, there is only one firm rule after all: what works works, and what doesn't doesn't.

Efficiency lesson

Like the contents of the last chapter, storytelling has more to do with effectiveness than efficiency: it's a tool to help your readers take your message in. If you keep the building blocks of stories at the back of your head when you write, it will help you structure your text into a flow where one part leads to the next. That flow is what pulls your readers along. It builds intention and purpose into a text that mostly consists of facts and figures. But there is an element of efficiency here as well. If you make *conflict-action-change* your mantra while writing, less effort will be needed to revise and sew the parts together to make a compelling argument.

Exercise: Pick out a good scientific paper that you found particularly engaging and easy to follow. Analyze it from a storytelling perspective. At the highest level, is the research question presented as a conflict— an obstacle that requires action? For a story to be compelling, the main conflict must be of great importance to the protagonist. How do the authors convince you of the importance of their research problem? In the section that describes how the study was set up, do they introduce each action as a response to a conflict—either the main conflict or a conflict that arises in the particular situation? At the end of the paper, where they discuss the results and state their conclusions, is it clear that the main conflict of the paper has been solved? Do they show how the state of knowledge changed as a result?

Exercise: Now, read your own paper with these questions in mind. Even though the paper you just analyzed may not have utilized all the building blocks of stories, there's nothing saying that you can't. Think about how you can build a dramatic arc and which scenes you should use to do it. Underline each action described in the text and ask yourself what conflict it is a response to. Have you described that conflict? Keep experimenting. This way of working is probably new to you, and it always takes time to master a new skill. If you don't immediately get the hang of the story perspective, maybe it will happen when you write your next paper, or the one after that.

84

Chapter 9

Revving up the revision

Nobody ever sat down at the keyboard and put all the right words in the right places right away. All authors edit, rearrange, and even rewrite their texts several times before they're satisfied with the result. It's important to realize that revision is not a question of correcting little mistakes. It cuts through all the stages of writing. In this chapter, we'll begin by making a plan for a three-step revision process. After that, our focus will move to polishing your paper to perfection.

Planning the revision process

Your text is exposed to several waves of criticism on its way from idea to finished manuscript. The first wave comes from the inner critic I talked about in Chapter 3, but others will have opinions too, and they will become more distant from you the further into the process you get. After a few rounds of comments from co-authors and scientific advisors, the peer review will even bring opinions from anonymous strangers. This constant flow of criticism can be disheartening to novice writers, but in time you'll realize that comments from people who read your text with fresh eyes are necessary for improving your manuscript to the level it deserves. However difficult it may seem when you read their comments, you should try to see these critics as your friends.

Since the revision moves through several stages and involves several people, a bit of project management will help you avoid losing valuable time during the final stages of writing. You would be well advised to make a time plan with the different steps of revision as milestones, and to inform your supervisors and co-authors ahead of time about when you need their input—especially if you are writing for a deadline, which is especially common with conference papers. The sooner the activities around your paper make their way into your colleagues' calendars, the smaller the risk for delays. Another important part in this is to inform them of how you want the revision process to work, so they can give you the type of comments you want.

I'm coming back to the three-step drafting process here. One of the main virtues of writing three drafts is that it forces you to invite feedback along the way. Whatever you do, avoid the classical mistake of working alone until you have written a complete draft. A finished draft opens up for comments on anything from wording and grammar to contents and disposition and you risk working through a very non-linear revision, constantly jumping between big issues and itty-bitty details. Another problem is that most people hesitate to suggest big changes to a manuscript that has an air of being finished, although big changes may be needed to lay a solid foundation for your paper. And when they do have the courage to comment on bigger issues, the only way to address those comments is to rewrite whole sections—sections that you have already polished into a finished draft. Working alone until you have written a complete draft is simply not an efficient way of working. Three-step drafting ensures that you get comments on contents and disposition early enough to avoid losing valuable momentum when you approach the finish line.

Start by informing your colleagues that you will hand them three completely different drafts. Tell them that the first will be a rough outline that should be revised with respect to contents and disposition only. If you don't tell them this, they will probably send your strawman draft back saying that it isn't a complete paper—please get back to me when you have something for me to read. You must make clear that you only want them to say if they think all the major parts of the paper are there and in the right order. The purpose at this stage is to have everyone agree on the message that you are about to send out into the world in the form of this paper. How should you motivate the work? How should you formulate the research question and describe your approach? Which are the central conclusions and which plots are necessary to support them? Having everyone onboard and agreeing to these most basic aspects of your paper will avoid confusion towards the end of the writing process; let alone major revisions of a text that you have already spent a lot of time editing.

When you have agreed on the contents and what goes where, inform your coauthors that the next version of the text will be intentionally sketchy. If you don't, your colleagues will send your rough draft back saying that your writing is very poor indeed. Ask them to give the text a quick read-through to see if you should give some parts less space, if other parts should be elaborated, and if the parts line up to form a coherent message. The purpose at this stage is to build a working line of argument.

Finally, when they receive the polished draft (and not before) it's time to revise for style and editorial quality. This is the first time you invite comments on wording, spelling and other elements of finesse. The point of this way of working is to keep your friends from giving too detailed feedback before it's needed—to focus on function before style.

Some people think this is an odd way to revise a text, but it's actually quite natural. Do you remember the architect designing a house at the beginning of Chapter 7? She would surely want to hear what her customers think about the situation of the building in relation to access roads and so on well before she has decided where to place doors and kitchen cabinets. That's why an architect will start by showing her customers a rough sketch and follow up with more detailed sketches as she develops the building—getting feedback on the fundamental elements before focusing on the details. This is exactly what the three-step approach to revision is about. It zooms from the broad brushstrokes towards the finer details.

When you make a time plan for the revision, you should obviously make room for the input of others as well as your own writing. Begin by finding out how much time you can reasonably spend writing. You probably have other duties, and it's usually wise to mix writing with other tasks anyway. Since very few people can write efficiently for days on end, you might want to limit your writing to mornings and deal with other tasks in the afternoon. Then start at the deadline and count backwards. How long do you need to write the polished draft? How much time do your coauthors need to take a look at it and give some final comments? And how long will it take to make the final edits before submitting it? The sum of these times gives you the latest date when you must have finished the polished draft. Put a milestone in your calendar there. Then continue your planning backwards through time. Add the time you need to write the rough draft to the time your coauthors need to comment on it and put another milestone in your calendar there. Finally, you will have an estimate of when you must start writing to be able to finish your manuscript in time.

Beware that a plan like this has no room for contingencies. Things can and will go wrong, so put some slack into your schedule just in case. The greatest risk for delays usually lies in the waiting time. When you hand a draft over to your colleagues, you also hand them the control of the process. If they don't prioritize working on your text, you may be in for a long wait before you see their comments. That's why it's so important to ask them to confirm the time plan at an early stage, making sure that there is room in their calendars for working on your drafts when you deliver them.

The first edit

When you have worked through the strawman and rough drafts—when all the information is there and in the right order, and you have drawn out your line of argument—it's time to take a critical look at how your text reads. This largely goes back to things we have already discussed, but I will touch on it here to remind you that these are things you usually have to go over several times before you're satisfied with your draft. No matter how experienced you are and how handy you are with your writer's toolbox, when you have let your first draft rest for a while you'll begin to see that it's far from finished. When you're writing, you develop a kind of tunnel vision that blocks out certain problems in the text. You gradually become blind to certain aspects of your writing. Those problems tend to pop out at you during the revision phase, and the good thing is that you now have the overview needed to solve them.

There are generally three types of problems to look out for at this stage: a disorganized text, a text that's difficult to understand, and a text that lacks flow. If you think that your first draft seems disorganized, the remedy is obviously to get it organized. The first question to ask is if you've done your housekeeping, making sure all the contents are under the headings where they belong. The next step is to go through the text and focus your writing as described in Chapter 7. Are you limiting each sentence to one thought, each paragraph to one idea? Focusing your text like this tends to untangle the most obvious knots in your line of argument.

But even a well-organized text may be difficult to understand. Besides gross violations of the rules of composition, the most common reason for this is that you've left out important information. This happens surprisingly often when we write. Interestingly, it seldom happens when we explain things orally. When you talk to people, you see their facial expressions and hear their little grunts of confirmation or confusion. If they don't follow you, you simply fill them in with more information before you move on. Writing doesn't involve this natural feedback, so you actively have to imagine the reader's reactions to what you tell her. Since it's difficult to underrate mind-reading as a means of communication, your job as an author is to *explicitly* give your reader all the information she needs to understand your work. It's often difficult to know how much information is just right, but one method is to imagine that you are sitting in front of someone who doesn't know the details of your work (your grandmother, for instance), and that you're explaining it to her. Ask yourself if she would understand what you wrote—at least sans the technical details—and, when you suspect that she wouldn't, go back and retell the problematic passage step by step without omitting any information. As a general rule of thumb, your readers need far more information to understand your work than you imagine.

The most common problem with early drafts, at least in my experience, is lack of flow. It's often due to a lack of text transitions, and this is another thing that tends to come naturally when you are explaining something orally. If a passage doesn't flow nicely, imagine that you're retelling it orally and note where you use transition words to connect clauses and sentences. Then bind the written text together in those places using transition words that match the scientific style. Another way to bind the text together is to start a sentence with something you have mentioned in the previous sentence, as I do in this sentence. You can also experiment with the tell-tell-tell technique to the same effect.

Another way to enhance the flow is to work on the story element of the text. Remember that every action in your text is taken to overcome a conflict of some sort, and that it probably leads to a change. When you have identified these parts in each passage, make sure they are presented in that order—conflict should lead to action, which should lead to change. The problem is when a passage describes several actions, which is especially common in Method sections. The trick is then to find the most natural way to order the actions one after the other. Close your eyes and try to see the different ways in which they could be connected. Are they a series of treatments that a sample has to undergo before it can be analyzed? If so, there is a temporal flow of actions and it probably makes sense to present them in chronological order. If you are describing how a laser beam is manipulated by optical components on its way to a measurement object, there's a spatial connection and it makes sense to describe the components in the order that the beam passes through them. There are of course other ways to organize the parts of your setup. You could describe your components in alphabetical order, in order of importance to the experiment, or in order of their physical size. I couldn't argue with you if you said that all these options are just as structured and logical as a chronological or spatial sequence, but logic isn't everything. We interpret the world through stories, and all these ways of creating a logical flow lack the story's way of having one situation lead to the next. This makes it more difficult for your readers to relate to them.

When you're working on the readability of your text, it's useful to think of it as a window onto the world.[1] In this classic approach to writing, what you write about is something you have seen, and the purpose of what you write is to put the reader in a position where she can see it, too—your text is the window through which she will be able to share your view of the world. For this to work, you must obviously organize the text and include all the information needed to understand it, but—crucially—the metaphor of the window emphasizes the visual aspect of explaining your message. Your text becomes more readable if you aim to *show* your readers something, for instance by acting as a tour guide and by using story elements in your writing. Keep this in mind as you go through your text.

The final edit

The next level in this top-down approach to revision focuses on details that are important for clarity, your professional voice, and something that I'll call the *punch* of your text. We are now definitely working at the level of sentences and words, and the problems that turn up here sort under the headings of style and correctness.

When you go through the details, a number of practical questions will arise. You may suddenly wonder if you really should spell acronyms in capital letters, and when you should put hyphens between words. These are questions about the correct use of English—rules that are non-negotiable and, fortunately, easy to find in a good dictionary. I won't go into them here. Instead, I will recommend that you get a copy of *the Elements of Style* by Strunk and White.[19] I would read it from cover to cover, letting the aha-moments wash over me, and then keep it close at hand when writing. In less than 100 small pages it lucidly presents the most important dos and don'ts of written English. Though some of its advice is a bit dated, it still serves its purpose for the majority of us that don't have a degree in English.

I'll turn to more general recommendations for style here. These are some areas where it's common to find room for improvement during the final edit:

- Tense
- Inconsistent use of acronyms
- Repetitive writing
- The passive voice
- Excessive use of nominalizations
- Verbose sentences

You're probably aware that the *tense* tells the reader if the actions you describe take place in the past, present or future. Since our readers are obviously reading about our research after it was done, the past tense is often the most intuitive choice, as in this example:

The air was filtered before the intake manifold.

This filtering is clearly over and done with by the time you write your paper, but you wouldn't break any strict rules if you wrote the same sentence in the present tense. Some authors prefer this as it gives the text a more direct, active quality:

The air is filtered before the intake manifold.

There is nothing that forbids you to use several tenses in your manuscript—in fact, you should. Tense orients your readers as to when the actions you describe occurred, and sometimes it makes obvious sense to mix two tenses, even in the same sentence:

The air is filtered before the intake manifold since previous experience showed this to reduce wear.

As the previous experience is previous to the investigation, it's correct to describe it in the past tense ("showed"). If the first part of the sentence were written in the past tense, we would push the second part another step into the past:

The air was filtered before the intake manifold since previous experience had shown this to reduce wear.

There are tense shifts that should be avoided. You shouldn't refer to actions that took place within the same timeframe using different tenses, like this:

The air is filtered before the intake manifold. It was then heated to 403 K.

Here, the actions of filtering and heating took place during the same investigation but are referred to in different tenses. If you do this, your readers lose their sense of time and cannot separate current actions from previous findings or future plans. To avoid confusion, always make a conscious decision about what tense to use where, then go through the text and check that you stuck to your decision.

There is also a deeper, less obvious aspect of tense, besides telling the reader when something happened. Read the following two sentences, which describe results from an experiment about multitasking:

Dual-task performance was inferior to single-task performance.

Dual-task performance is inferior to single-task performance.

Do you sense a difference? It may be subtle, but the second version is more definite. Using the present tense, you generalize. You tell the reader that you are more certain about your claims than when you use the past tense, and this means that you should choose different tenses in different sections of your paper. The recommendation is to use the past tense in the Results section, because you are then laying out the evidence for the reader without making generalizations (and, yes, the first version of the sentence above is taken from a Results section.) The exception is when you describe figures and tables, since the reader is obviously looking at them when she is reading. A reference to a figure might read something like this:

The signal increased with the laser fluence until it reached a plateau. Figure 1 displays the fluence curve and the transition to the plateau region at 1.5 J/cm².

Here, the results are described in the past tense (increased, reached) and the figure in the present tense (displays).

When you move on to the discussion, you are generalizing from your results, explaining their significance. Here, you should use the present tense:

The trends are consistent among the three cases, indicating that the soot formation rate is fairly constant under these conditions.

Here, the text explains what the findings mean, which is why it's written in present tense (are, indicating, is). Using the word "indicating", you tell the reader that you're confident that the conclusion is correct. If you want to signal that other interpretations are possible, you might use softer wordings like "it is possible that" or "this may be due to"—but still in the present tense.

In general, you are recommended to use the following primary tenses in the different sections of your paper:[20]

- **Abstract:** past tense, since you're outlining an investigation that's already completed.
- **Introduction:** present tense, since it includes background information that's generally accepted in your field, and since you are explaining why your research is important.
- **Method:** past tense, since you're describing what you *did*.
- **Results:** past tense, since you're referring to data already obtained, and you are not making generalizations yet.
- **Discussion:** present tense in the parts where you're explaining the significance of your results.

- **Conclusion:** a combination of tenses to highlight past results, present significance, and future implications.

As I mentioned before, there are good reasons for mixing tenses within the sections. Even if you choose to write the introduction in the present tense, for example, you will occasionally switch to future and past tense when the text looks forward or backward from that reference point. By "primary tense", I simply mean the tense you choose for each section—the tense that is most common there.

The second point on the list is inconsistent use of acronyms. As previously discussed, when you use an acronym, you should introduce it the first time it appears and then consistently use it instead of the combination of words it replaces. This is as easy to remember as buying milk on the way home from work—and just as easy to forget. As text doesn't grow linearly (especially not if you draft in three steps), it's often difficult to know if you're using an acronym for the first time. This is the reason why I bring the problem up in the chapter on revision. When you're editing, you have an overview that makes it easy to keep track of this.

Repetitive writing is a problem that takes many forms. It could be a particular word that appears several times in sentences that follow each other, that two or more sentences in a row begin with the same combination of words, or that you repeat a similar sentence structure over and over. This is difficult to spot while writing, but it tends to pop out at you when you read. The solution is of course to exchange the recurrent word with a synonym, or to vary the sentence structure.

Some take the fear of repeating words to extremes and live by the rule not to use the same word more than once on every page.[1] This often gives a strained impression, since you quickly run out of suitable synonyms, especially for specialized scientific terms. Once you have used the term *carbon monoxide* on a page, for example, you might use *carbonous oxide* and *carbonyl*, but soon have to resort to abstract phrases like *the odorless gas* or the *diatomic molecule*. Such synonymania can be both comical and confusing, especially in complex passages where it must be clear that what you are referring to over and over is, in fact, the same thing.

To avoid confusion, do not to replace terminology and important concepts with synonyms. It's perfectly fine to write *carbon monoxide* over and over—no one will think twice about it. Readers are not as sensitive to repetition of key words as you might think, so in the choice between clarity and variation, choose clarity. The type of words that tend to sound repetitive are linking words like "however" or "thus", or more general words like "problem", which can be replaced with "challenge", "difficulty", or "hurdle" without risking confusion.

It is more disruptive to the flow of your text when the same sentence *structure* is repeated over and over. If you have lined up several short sentences in a row the remedy is often to join them, at least if they convey the same thought. If the text still feels repetitive, look at how you build your sentences. In this one,

The flu often breaks out in late autumn.

the subject comes at the beginning. If you want to break a line of several such sentences, you could simply move the temporal element to the front:

Late autumn often brings an outbreak of flu.

This is just one example. Similar sentences are boring. Try to vary your writing. To break the monotony, perhaps you could pose a rhetorical question: are rows of short clauses like the ones just before this sentence problematic? Yes, they tend to give a dull impression, and the remedy is spelled *variation*. Variation makes a text lively, whether it be in sentence structure, sentence type, or length.

The most general advice you will find in any guide to writing is probably this: avoid using the *passive voice* whenever possible. Strong, active verbs make a text clear and easy to understand, whereas passive verbs tend to make sentences long and vague. Unfortunately, budding researchers often have an affinity for wordy, passive sentences. Even more unfortunately, many never grow out of it. Some even think that it's unprofessional to write in the active form. Here is one example of a passive sentence:

Fuel is transferred by the spray towards the combustion chamber wall where it is displaced back towards the center.

This sentence describes what happens to fuel inside an engine using the verbs *transfer* and *displace*. We know that they are written in the passive form since they are preceded by a form of the verb *be* (the fuel *is* transferred and *is* displaced), and since the verbs end with *-ed*. But if one thing is acted on by another, why can't the other thing act on the first? And, while we're at it, why don't we beef our verbs up to stronger, more specific ones?

> *The spray transports fuel to the combustion chamber wall, which redirects it towards the center.*

The verbs *transport* and *redirect* give a stronger sense of action, especially when we use them in their active forms. The second sentence is not only shorter, it also gives a clearer sense of what happens to the fuel.

Now look at the following sentence:

> *In a previous study, it was demonstrated that the phenomenon is due to flash boiling.*

Does it use active or passive verbs? Before you read on, take a few seconds to think about how you could make it simpler and clearer.

Here is one suggestion:

> *A previous study showed that flash boiling causes the phenomenon.*

Again, active verbs make sentences shorter and clearer. Both are desirable features of scientific writing—in fact, they are desirable in almost any form of writing, epic poetry perhaps being the only exception. To spot whether a sentence is written in the active or passive form, try to see whether the action in it is received or performed. As a rule of thumb, when you find a noun that receives action, emphasizing the noun that performs the action tends to improve the text.

But if the active form is so much better, why do we have a passive form in the first place? The simple answer is that it fills an important function, although that function turns out to be a bit hairy to explain. My favorite explanation is Steven Pinker's analogy with a spotlight.[1] Putting it simply, the active voice puts the spotlight on the main doer in the sentence. If there are other doers in the sentence, it's better to express their doings in the passive voice—otherwise you will pull the spotlight from what's driving the action. As any abstract idea, this is best illustrated by an example:

Alexander the Great crushed free city-states and was resented by the Greeks as a tyrant, but he revered the gods of Egypt and was welcomed in that land as a deliverer.

Although this sentence gives us the opinions of the Greeks and Egyptians in the passive voice, it isn't difficult to follow what it tells us. Now, let's put it in the active voice throughout:

Alexander the Great crushed free city-states and the Greeks resented him as a tyrant, but he revered the gods of Egypt and the Egyptians welcomed him as a deliverer.

Did you notice how this version made your focus jump back and forth between the main character (Alexander), the Greeks and the Egyptians? The more complex the text, the more confusing such constant switching of focus becomes. The first version keeps the spotlight on what Alexander did by using the passive voice to describe the opinions of the Greeks and Egyptians. So, while the active voice makes a text direct and "vigorous" (as Strunk and White put it), the passive voice is often needed to avoid confusion about the subject of complex sentences—it prevents the spotlight from jumping all over the stage when you want it to stay on the main doer.

Another legitimate (though unfortunate) reason to use the passive voice is that you're often forced to do so when writing in the third person. As we have said, large parts of the scientific community are phobic about using the words *I* and *we*. They would much rather refer to themselves as *the authors* or, even better, avoid mentioning themselves at all. When you remove the doer from a sentence you have no choice but to use the passive voice, but keep in mind that it gives your text a feeble impression. Just as a politician may try to evade responsibility by saying "mistakes were made" instead of "*we* made mistakes", a scientist saying "measurements were made" gives the impression that he's trying to distance himself from his work.

So, there is one good reason and one not-so-good (but legitimate) reason to use the passive voice. This means you can't completely rid your text of passives. The point is this: don't bog your text down with vague writing just for the sake of sounding scientific. Go through your text, underline all the passives and ask yourself if they are really necessary. If you analyze the first examples in this sub-section you'll see how the active form often results in distinct, concise writing. Keep the passives only when they help you to write more clearly by keeping the reader's eyes on what's important.

Another common problem in scientific writing is a phenomenon called *nominalization*. The most common form of nominalization is when you turn a verb into a noun and let the noun represent the action. For example, you are nominalizing if you make an *analysis* of your data instead of *analyzing* them. Nominalization is not incorrect in itself but, as we have seen, strong, active verbs make a text easier to read. Here is another example of a verb buried in a nominalization:

> *Concentration measurements were carried out in situ.*

Yes, you got it. Measurement is a nominalization. Putting the action in the corresponding verb makes the sentence shorter and clearer:

> *We measured concentrations in situ.*

If your editor is outraged by the frivolous use of the personal pronoun *we* in this sentence, the second-best option is to resort to a formulation like:

> *Concentrations were measured in situ.*

Although this sentence is passive, the action is at least expressed in a verb.

At first glance, a nominalization may seem to give your text a more objective, academic quality, but very often it just adds hot air. You can form nouns from other word classes too, like adjectives or even other nouns, by adding a suffix like *-ity*, *-tion*, or *-ism*. When you turn the adjective *implacable* into *implacability*, for example, or the noun *atheist* into *atheism*, you're making a nominalization. As everything we have invented in the language, these constructions have their legitimate use, but often they make your text abstract and difficult to relate to. Readers want to see action and who performs it—nominalizations make both difficult. The writing scholar Helen Sword calls them "zombie nouns" because they "cannibalize active verbs, suck the lifeblood from adjectives and substitute abstract entities for human beings".[21] I can't resist quoting one of her example sentences, which contains no fewer than seven nominalizations:

> *The* proliferation *of* nominalizations *in a discursive* formation *may be an* indication *of a* tendency *toward* pomposity *and* abstraction.

Sounds very academic, doesn't it? But can you figure out who did what in this sentence? One of a few possible interpretations is

> *Writers who overload their sentences with nominalizations tend to sound pompous and abstract.*

So, go through your text, look for those little suffixes and eye them suspiciously. In the interest of avoidance of the suspicion that you have a tendency toward pomposity, blow life into your nominalizations by turning them back into spry verbs, colorful adjectives, and concrete nouns.

This goes back to what I said in the previous section about your text being a window onto the world. They say that two thirds of our brains deal with visual impressions, and that's the key to understanding why passive writing and nominalizations often become problems. As vision is our dominant sense, you should strive to make your readers *see* what you tell them. Show them what's done and who does it. If you remove these concrete elements from your text and replace them with a sludge of passives and nominalizations, you dim your readers' mental vision of your message and, gradually, put them to sleep.

The last point on our list is *verbose sentences*. Scientists strive to write concisely and to the point, but often have to edit carefully to get there. In early drafts, it's common to find the same information stated several times in the same paragraph, or even in the same sentence. Reading your text carefully, you'll find words that don't do anything except to make sentences longer. This happens to all of us.

When you read your text, boil each paragraph down to its essence in your mind. Ask yourself what's happening in it and which information is needed to explain it. Then try to think of the best way to convey that information as briefly and simply as possible. When you have done this, go through the text once more, sentence by sentence, asking yourself if there are any words that don't serve a purpose. You will be surprised at how often this happens. Look at this sentence, copied with permission from an early draft:

The intake air charge is heated before it enters the intake manifold.

When you casually read it, you don't see the redundant information, but if you look actively, you will find that it reads better if you cut out some freeloaders:

The air is heated before the intake manifold.

Obviously, the air is intake air—you don't have to tell the reader since the sentence already says that it's going into the intake manifold. And why do you need to add the little word "charge", when it doesn't add any crucial information to the fact that air is going into a manifold? By the way, you probably understood that the air *enters* the manifold without me explicitly saying so in the second version. Isn't this an improvement?

Chances are that most of the sentences in your first draft can be refined like this, and it does wonders to the readability when you do. Still, weeding out unnecessary words is a step in the revision process that many pass over completely, at least in my experience of writing with different sets of people over the years. This is what Strunk and White say about wordy sentences in rule 17 of *The Elements of Style*. The title of the rule is *Omit Needless Words*—in itself an excellent illustration of its tenor:

> *Vigorous writing is concise. A sentence should contain no unnecessary words, a paragraph no unnecessary sentences, for the same reason that a drawing should contain no unnecessary lines and a machine no unnecessary parts. This requires not that the writer make all sentences short, or avoid all detail and treat subjects only in outline, but that every word tell.*[20]

That's the essence of avoiding verbose sentences: every word must tell. That's what I referred to as the punch at the beginning of the chapter.

Even the most experienced authors have to trim their texts to improve their punch. Stephen King tells us he has a formula for this part of the revision process:[8]

$$2^{nd} \; Draft = 1^{st} \; Draft - 10 \; \%.$$

The formula grew out of a lesson he learned as a high school kid when, apparently, he had scoffed a teacher in his unofficial school newspaper. As a punishment, the principal sent him to work as a reporter at the weekly newspaper in Lisbon, Maine, to turn his "restless pen" to more constructive channels. When he handed in his first piece there, the editor picked up a black pen and silently began to cross out words in the manuscript. It was a revelation, King said— why had no English teacher ever done this? The text shrank and improved. When the editor handed the text back, he said "I only took out the bad parts, you know. Most of it's pretty good." Then he said what King considers to be the most valuable writing lesson of his life: "When you write a story, you're telling yourself the story. When you rewrite, your main job is taking out all the things that are *not* the story." [8]

Take that to heart. Read your text slowly to find all the little words, phrases, and even paragraphs that are not the story. Surgically remove them. And I suggest you print King's formula and pin it to your wall.

Handing the text over to others

After these steps, your polished draft is as good as you can make it on your own. At this stage, it's easy to believe that your efforts have elevated it to utter perfection, but as you hand it over to your coauthors, rest assured that they will find flaws you have missed and come up with ideas that you didn't think of.

It's quite natural to be vulnerable to critical comments when you have worked with a text for a long time. The first reaction is often to defend yourself, but it's better to fight that impulse. Hear your friends out instead. When you do, you will see your paper from new perspectives. We all have blind spots, especially after scrutinizing a text for a long time, and receiving criticism is a natural part of improving it even further.

But if I can still expect plenty of comments on my polished draft, you say, why should I spend all this time improving it? Why not let my coauthors pull their share of the load by giving them a rougher draft? Well, you could, but when several people edit and add details to a text, it may not improve the overall style at all. Good prose is never written by a committee. You want to keep your coauthors from proofreading to help them focus on deeper text problems. Polishing your draft before your coauthors see it is really about staying in control over your text and making their comments as useful as possible.

But the revision isn't over when you have collected comments and ideas from your coauthors. Sometimes we think of the anonymous peer review as the part when complete strangers get to complain about our work, but it's actually one of the most important parts of revision. When you write a paper, you start with an idea that exists inside your own head, and your aim is to put that idea into the head of somebody else. When you think about it, it's baffling that you can even accomplish this by lining up alphanumeric symbols on a page—and that's probably why writing is so hard. Thinking isn't linear in the way text is, so you have to remodel your complex network of thoughts into strings of words before readers can absorb them. No wonder it requires a critical look to make sure it's possible to understand what you mean. This happens in three steps. The first is when your inner critic tries to see where an outsider would need extra guidance to follow your train of thought. The second is when you ask your coauthors how well you succeeded with this. The peer review is the final test—you are now putting your text in the hands of people who have no prior knowledge of your research. They don't know how you came up with your idea and why you decided to conduct the study as you did. This is the first time somebody reads your text with completely fresh eyes. If you haven't explained your ideas and motivations well enough, your peer reviewers will struggle to understand your line of argument, so don't see their comments as complaints—they are really just pointing to areas that need more work before your paper effectively explains your thoughts to an audience outside your narrow circle of colleagues.

Revision as a process of learning

Writing is a craft and, as with any craft, you learn it through practice. You don't learn to write as much as you *discover* how to do it. You try expressing what you want to say and then read the result to check if it worked. If it didn't, you try another way and keep at it until you're satisfied.

Getting constructive feedback on your texts is one of the best ways to increase your rate of discovery. The question is, how do you make the feedback as constructive as possible? The main thing I'd like to point out is that we're only susceptible to feedback while we're actually working with a text. Comments received after it's finished have no demonstrated effect on your development as a writer.[22] In other words, you need comments long before you hand in a complete draft, and this is why I advocate the three-step model both for drafting and revising your paper. Dividing the work into three packages you'll obtain comments on all the important aspects of your text at the time when you are dealing with them, increasing the chances that the lessons will stick.

Another useful way to receive early feedback and climb faster on the learning curve is to form a response group. This is a group of peers (in your case, probably other PhD students) that commit to reading and providing feedback on each other's texts. It may sound strange to ask for feedback from people who don't know much more about writing than yourself, but their role is not to be expert writing instructors. You just want them to say which parts of your text they like and which they think need more work—and they only need to be capable readers to do that. Another advantage is that you get to read *their* texts with a critical eye. When you do, you get a valuable chance to reflect on what works in a text, what doesn't, and why.

Participating in a response group inevitably means that you have to offer comments to your friends. Prepare them well. The aim should obviously be to inspire, not to hurt, so comment on the text and your impressions of it, not your friends' writing skills. Instead of saying that someone forgot a crucial point, tell him that *the text* would be stronger if that information were included. Or, rather than telling him how poorly *he* wrote a passage, tell him that *you* find the passage difficult to understand. You should work like a coach and let him discover areas where he needs to put in extra work, but not give detailed instructions. Trust his abilities to solve the problems himself. Unfortunately, it's not unusual that supervisors break this trust by making substantial edits and even rewriting parts of their students' texts. This may be necessary if a text is not in a publishable state immediately before a deadline, but even if it improves a paper, it seldom improves the author. Authors very rarely go through the edited text, comparing it to the original, analyzing why the changes were needed. To support learning, the feedback should have a longer perspective than the next deadline—it should aim at developing the author as well as the text. And edits should always point to specific issues. If you show how a passive formulation works better in the active form and then ask the author to find other places in the text where he can make the same improvement, he will begin to learn about writing in the active form. If you edit all the passives, he won't.

Here's a suggestion for how you could prepare your feedback on a friend's text. Start by reading it from beginning to end, jotting down your spontaneous impressions. The first time is the only time you read the text with fresh eyes and if you constantly interrupt your reading with reflections, you won't get a fair impression. The next step is to go through your comments and look for cause and effect. *Why* do you like some parts, and why don't you like some others? Are they too long? Is something missing? Is there a lack in structure? To be helpful, your comments should be as specific as possible. As you formulate them, make sure to focus on function and contents before you turn to structure and style. If you don't actively force yourself to comment on the complex aspects of the text, your feedback will gravitate towards simple errors.

We all know how easy it is to spot the parts of a text we don't like. They almost pop out at us. It's much harder to identify parts that we like, and harder still to understand *why* we like them. The problem with negative feedback is that it only teaches us what not to do, whereas positive feedback enforces our skills and provides us with a repertoire of techniques to develop. Strive to find positive aspects in your friends' texts and to explain why you like them. When you point to something negative, explain why you think it is problematic and give hints about how you think it could be improved.

To summarize, in many ways, revision is the most important part of the writing process. It's the time you spend evaluating your work, reflecting on what works and what doesn't. It's the time you spend learning the craft. The worst mistake you can make if you want to develop as a writer is to rush through this. Invite feedback at all stages of writing, because feedback and reflection are the two horses that pull you up the learning curve.

Efficiency lesson

It may seem like most of what we have covered here has little to do with efficiency, but keep in mind that a well-planned revision process is quicker than one where you and your coauthors improvise your steps at each turn.

From a longer-term perspective, revision is an important part of learning the craft and thereby improves your efficiency over time. As you learn your chops, you will tend to write better papers faster. But it's true that revision is mostly about improving the text. It starts with showing that you can use English correctly and that you are able to express yourself clearly. It continues with refining your prose—the rhythm, motion, and punch of the text. The aim is to come across as a pro. Rejoice in the feedback you receive, because that feedback, over time, is what turns you into one.

Exercise: Go through your draft, look for monotonous passages and actively try to find ways to improve them by varying the sentence structure.

Exercise: Go through your draft and look for places where you have used the passive voice. Sometimes this is motivated, but often it's just a bad habit. In those cases, rewrite the sentences in the active form.

Exercise: In the same manner, go through your manuscript and underline all nominalizations. Change them into verbs or whatever word class they originated from and see if the text improves.

Exercise: Now, actively think of ways to boil your paragraphs and sentences down to their essence. Choose your words carefully and actively try to cut the number of words down. Chances are you will be amazed that you could write so well!

Chapter 10

Writing towards your PhD

Throughout most of this book, I have looked at writing from a perspective of productivity. I have talked about strategies and tools that help you streamline the process and, eventually, write better papers, faster.

But there is another perspective on writing that, in many ways, is much more important for you as a researcher. Since writing is essentially a way of organizing your thoughts, it's a central part of your thinking process. Learning to write scientific text is a way to learn scientific thinking. These days, when research tends to be externally funded, most of the thinking around research ideas takes place before the application for funding is submitted. When you enter the picture as a PhD student, most of the remaining work amounts to taking measurements in the lab. Unfortunately, writing is often your only chance to get involved in higher-level thinking around your research. This means you shouldn't put it off until later.

In this chapter I'll discuss how you can get started with your writing the very moment you begin your PhD studies. We will also take a look at how the PhD thesis differs from the papers we have focused on so far. Finally, I will summarize what I hope you'll bring with you from this little book as you go ahead with your writing.

The research plan

There are several reasons to start writing the very minute you embark on your journey towards the PhD. The first has probably dawned slowly on you over the last few chapters: writing is a skill that none of us is born with. Many take a course in scientific writing in the hope that it will provide them with tools and tricks that instantly turn them into full-fledged writers—many may even have picked up this book with that expectation. Tools and tricks exist and they help you put a manuscript together, but the truth is that neither courses nor books will help you turn them into skills. Skills are developed through practice. What's worse is that it takes time, so don't wait with writing until you have finished your first experiment—it may take a year or two before you get that far. You should find a way to create regular writing habits already from the outset, because writing regularly is what's needed to develop the skill. Sooner than you think, you will be expected to write a whole thesis.

Another important reason to write from day one is that it's the best way to claim ownership of your PhD project. At the start, your supervisor will probably put a project description or a project plan in your hands, hoping that it will help you figure out what to do over the next few years. But that document is based on your supervisor's thoughts and background knowledge. To take the driver's seat in your project, you must build your own thoughts and knowledge, and writing is one of the best methods to do that. When writing about your research you learn to think like a researcher. When writing, you are working out everything from the motivation for your research to how to build an argument based on your data. You are structuring and restructuring your thoughts, working analytically throughout every step. In short, writing is a form of thinking that both develops your text and your skills as a scientific thinker.

But how do you write about your research before you've got any results? Easy. If you compare your project to a building, the results are just the bricks that you use to build it. But research is not bricklaying—it's architecture. Even though bricks will make up much of the finished building, without a plan they are just a pile of material. More than anything, a beautiful building is the result of conscious design. So is your project and, one day, your thesis.

The first thing that happens during your PhD studies is usually that you're asked to study the relevant literature. This is a good place to start your scientific writing. The outcome of a literature study can take many forms, but at some stage you will probably have a list of brief descriptions of the central contents of papers you have read. Some of the items in this literature summary may be directly relevant to your research problem, others may cover general background knowledge. Sort them accordingly. Then go through the summary and transfer the items into your project description. If your supervisor didn't give you a project description, this is when you should ask for it. Relate the items in your literature summary to the research question that you're supposed to answer. Read your text and ask yourself if it's structured to lead a reader from an overall perspective of your field towards a more detailed picture of your research. It should read like the introduction section of a paper but be more elaborate and go deeper. Edit the document until you have a coherent, readable text. Gradually, it will grow into something that covers the knowledge in the field as it is described in the literature, but in your own words and in relation to your own research question. It will also identify gaps in the knowledge, some of which your research aims to fill. In short, it will grow into the story about your project.

As I have said before, don't keep your writing to yourself. Feedback is essential for learning, and you're mostly writing this document to learn. Show what you have written to your supervisor, mentor, colleagues, or anyone who is willing to give comments on your writing. Learn from the comments, rework your text and continue to write.

After you have drawn up the background and convinced yourself that you understand the need for what you're about to do, it's time to describe your approach to the research problem. What methods will you use? How can you design experiments or other types of studies to obtain relevant and useful data? Even if you don't have detailed ideas yet, put your thoughts into the document, discuss them and work them into a battle plan of sorts—a plan outlining how you intend to overcome the obstacles that stand between you and the goal of answering your research question. This is the next part of your story.

The document you're writing has now turned into a research plan: it motivates your research by identifying a knowledge gap and explains how you intend to fill that gap with your research. And as you have seen, you can start writing it from day one of your research studies. This way, you'll always have a scientific text to work on—even when your first paper is still months or years away. As you read more papers and deepen your understanding of what your research is about, you will add to the research plan and revise it. The plan will put you in a much better position for navigating your project towards your PhD degree. What's more, a few years down the line, your research plan will have grown into the opening chapters of your PhD thesis. Over that period, your little document will have given you ample opportunity to write scientific text on a regular basis, get feedback on what you write, and learn the craft *before* you face the deadline of submitting a finished thesis.

How a thesis differs from a paper

When you get to the stage when you're expected to write the rest of your thesis, it's helpful to know what a thesis *is* and how it differs from the papers we have focused on in this book. In most places, the PhD thesis is a monograph—a book where you describe and discuss your research. In some places, the thesis is a summary document with the papers attached at the end. This has the advantage that most of the papers are published by the time you defend your thesis, meaning that you have demonstrated that your work meets the quality standards in your field. That will make it difficult for a committee to fail you. Most of what I'm saying about the thesis in this section applies to both monographs and summaries.

Originally, a master's degree was a license to practice and a doctor's degree was a license to teach at the university level. You obviously need deep knowledge to teach with authority, and one of the purposes of a PhD thesis is to show your readers that you have that knowledge.[23] Another purpose is to demonstrate that you have the skills needed to do research. A PhD degree is like a driver's license for research, and the thesis is the exam paper that your grading committee will use to judge if you have learned your skills. So, while a thesis usually contains more or less the same parts as a scientific paper, the purpose of the thesis is entirely different from that of a paper.

A paper is all about what the data can tell us. The purpose of everything you write in it is to demonstrate that the conclusions you draw from your data are valid. A thesis, on the other hand, is all about you. You write it to show that your knowledge and skills are at the level expected of a professional researcher. For this reason, you must describe everything in your thesis at a much deeper level than if you wrote a paper. Even if you expect your audience to know everything you write about, the idea is to show them that *you* know it. Let's go through the anatomy of a thesis as we did with a scientific paper in Chapter 6.

The first part is the *Introduction* chapter, which is supposed to motivate your research by spelling out your research problem and explaining why it's important. If you were writing a paper, this part would describe the related literature and present the research question. In a thesis, the literature review must be both broader and deeper than that. As a PhD, you are expected to possess a broad knowledge of your general field as well as a deep knowledge within a specific part of that field, so it isn't sufficient to just summarize or mention relevant studies. You must organize the background knowledge in a coherent and interesting way. It's important to show that you can identify important research trends and point to potential knowledge gaps that could motivate new research. You should also show that you're able to evaluate the contributions of other researchers and, if you are critical of them, justify your criticism. If there is a theory part in this chapter, the purpose is not merely to prepare the reader for an upcoming analysis, but to demonstrate that *you* fully understand the theoretical concepts that are central to your work. This is how you show that you're in command of your subject.

The next part of the thesis deals with *Methods*. The purpose is to show that you understand and master all the practical elements involved in your studies, whether they were experiments, observational studies, method development, or computer simulations. It isn't sufficient just to state that you have used a particular measurement instrument, for instance; you must explain how it works. Instead of just describing your analysis techniques, you must explain their fundamental principles, including a critical discussion of their limitations. What can you do with them and what can't you do? A thesis goes deeper than a paper, in every aspect.

The *Results and Discussion* parts will take on different shapes depending on the format of your thesis. If you're writing a monograph, they will include a full account of the data and analyses that underlie your contribution. If you're writing a summary with papers, the summary must still describe your results with references to your papers and, more importantly, relate your findings to each other and to the knowledge in the literature as a whole. This is called a synthesis.

The synthesis brings us to the part of the thesis where you define your scientific contribution. Sometimes, this part comes at the end of the discussion, sometimes it's a separate chapter at the end of the

112

thesis. As the PhD degree is awarded for an original contribution to knowledge, one of the most important purposes of your thesis is to demonstrate that you have made such a contribution. You started out formulating a research question based on a knowledge gap that you had identified in the literature. Here, you put the pieces of your work together and formulate higher-level conclusions. Hopefully, they answer the research question, completely or partly, and you should discuss how they do so. It's also important to relate your results to the work of others and clearly spell out how you have advanced the knowledge in your field. This part may seem intimidating, but you don't have to be shortlisted for the Nobel Prize to have made a valuable contribution. You did something new, didn't you? Something that nobody did before. That's an original contribution to knowledge and explaining why and how you did it is what earns you your degree.

Besides defining your contribution, you should also discuss the limitations of your work. The long-term goal of science is to establish general knowledge—knowledge that can be used to explain, interpret, predict or control things around us in a general way. This means that it's important to make valid generalizations in your research, but also to discuss the limitations of your generalizations. Sometimes, this goes under the somewhat confusing heading of *Future work*. What future work, you may ask—I'm about to finish my thesis and who knows what I will be doing a year from now? But it doesn't necessarily mean that *you* will do that future work. What you are telling the reader under this heading is simply that you are aware that your contribution is incomplete, however valuable it may be. There are still parts of your research problem that need further study.

In short, the contribution is a synthesis between your collected work and the greater body of knowledge in your field. It explains why and in what way that knowledge has changed as a result of your work. From now on, when your successors write their background chapters, they will face a different situation because they have to consider *your* contribution when they write about their own.

And unto the horizon…

After reading this book, I hope you have seen that writing is not a mysterious ability that cannot be learnt. It's a skill and, as any skill, it grows with application.

To become a proficient writer, you must become comfortable with writing. This involves finding habits that help you produce text. It also involves finding a structured way to build your text, and times and places for writing that help you focus on what you do.

It also helps to build a repertoire of tools and techniques for shaping your text into a readable scientific paper. Some of them have been covered in this book, but you may pick up others from colleagues and supervisors. You will probably invent some yourself.

Whether you are writing a paper or a thesis—or any other text that you put a reasonable amount of work into—share it with your response group. Listen to their comments and learn. Repay them by providing useful, constructive criticism on their texts. Learning together is not only faster, it's also much more fun.

All writers must read, so read papers and ask yourself questions when you do. Don't limit your questions to the scientific contents—ask about the writing too. Take notice when you find a paper that you particularly like. What can you learn about writing from this author?

Good writing has a pleasant, seductive quality. It gives you the feeling that not a word is out of place, that everything is there for a reason. It's like watching your team score in a good game of hockey. There may be a deft skating maneuver, a sudden lateral pass to set the goalie off balance, and a wrist shot that puts the puck firmly in the net. It's hard, but it looks easy. Good writing is just like that. It pulls you into its flow and surprises you with its clarity. Good writing lets you know that you're in the hands of a professional who knows how to explain complex ideas without confusing you—not an amateur who's showing off by making things look more difficult than they are.

I hope you will find the advice in this book useful in your continued writing. Now, write. Learn the craft. Aim to make every word tell. It will pay off, not only in more citations, but also in the sheer joy of learning to write well.

Author's thanks

Writing a book like this is both a way to summarize your own thoughts, and to pass on what others have taught you during the years. It would be impossible to mention each and every one who helped me develop my writing, so I'll settle with thanking all teachers and friends who, in one way or another, managed to rub parts of their skills off on me.

That said, there are a few friends that I want to thank especially for their help with the drafts of this book. They have helped me see parts that needed elaboration and parts that needed trimming. They have also helped me kill a few of my darlings, as William Faulkner would have put it. When you are particularly pleased with your writing in a certain passage, it's usually a sign that it will come across as particularly contrived. It's almost uncanny how friends who are reading your text with fresh eyes will home in on those passages and help you realize how much better the text would do without them. However painful it is, taking your darlings out inevitably strengthens your text.

I am especially grateful to Mirjam Godskesen and Lene Nordrum for their extensive comments on the first draft. Mirjam actually inspired me to write parts of this book through her excellent *Academic Writing Bootcamp* in Denmark. Lene has insights into English and writing that most of us can only dream of, and a rare ability to make grammar fun. I am also happy to have her as one of my partners in crime producing the podcast *The Good, the Bad, and the Ugly of Writing in Academia*.

Sebastian Verhelst and Paul Miles read the second draft in its entirety. Sebastian provided the valuable impressions of a colleague who might use what I've written to actually supervise PhD students. Paul is a longtime friend who has always impressed me with his ability to write clearly about motley topics, and whose general wisdom I find

116

unsurpassed. Thank you both! Thanks also to Jens Larsen for cheering me on on the final stretch.

Of course, any flaws remaining in the text are entirely my own.

Finally, and as always, I am eternally grateful to my wife, Gunnel, and my son, Carl-Johan, for being there. Without you, nothing that I do would make much sense.

References

1. Pinker S. The sense of style: The thinking person's guide to writing in the 21st century. London: Penguin Books; 2014.
2. George E. Write on! New York: HarperCollins e-books; 2009.
3. Watson JM, Strayer DL. Supertaskers: Profiles in extraordinary multitasking ability. Psychonomic Bulletin & Review 2010; 17(4): 479-485.
4. Schulte, B. Work interruptions can cost you 6 hours a day. An efficiency expert explains how to avoid them. The Washington Post. 2015; Jun 1.
5. Fried, J. Why work doesn't happen at work. TED: Ideas worth spreading. Available from: http://www.ted.com/talks/jason_fried_why_work_doesn_t_h appen_at_work/.
6. Solomon L, Rothblum E. Academic procrastination: Frequency and cognitive-behavioural correlates. Journal of Counseling Psychology 1984; 31(4): 503-509.
7. McEwan I. On writing & inspiration. Knopf Doubleday Publishing Group. Available from: https://m.youtube.com/watch?v=o9LZfX3Y8TI/.
8. King, S. On writing: A memoir of the craft. New York: Scribner; 2000.
9. Gardiner M, Kearns H. The ABCDE of writing: Coaching high-quality high-quantity writing. International Coaching Psychology Review 2012; 7(2): 237-249.
10. Boice R. Contingency management in writing and the appearance of creative ideas: Implications for the treatment of writing blocks. Behaviour Research and Therapy 1983; 21(5): 537-543.
11. Murray R. How to write a thesis, 4th Ed. London: Open University Press; 2017.

118

12. Swales JM, Feak CB. Academinc writing for graduate students, 2nd Ed. Ann Arbor: University of Michigan press; 2004.
13. Endler JA. Natural selection on color patterns in Poecilia reticulata. Evolution 1980; 34(1): 76-91.
14. Yamamoto S, Humble T, Tanaka M. Chimpanzees' flexible targeted helping based on an understanding of conspecifics' goals. PNAS 2012; 109(9): 3588-3592.
15. Sahoo D, Miles PC, Trost J, Leipertz A. The impact of fuel mass, injection pressure, ambient temperature, and swirl ratio on the mixture preparation of a pilot injection. SAE International Journal of Engines 2013; 6(3).
16. Boyd B. On the origin of stories: Evolution, cognition, and fiction. Cambridge: Harvard University Press; 2010.
17. Cron L. Wired for story: The writer's guide to using brain science to hook readers from the very first sentence. New York: Ten Speed Press; 2012.
18. Carroll, L. Through the looking-glass. London: Puffin Books; 2010.
19. Strunk W, White EB. The elements of style, 4th Ed. New York: Longman; 2000.
20. University of Melbourne. Using tenses in acientific writing. Available from: https://services.unimelb.edu.au/_data/assets/pdf_file/0009/471294/Using_tenses_in_scientific_writing_Update_051112.pdf
21. Sword H. Zombie nouns. The New York Times. 2012; Jul 23.
22. Pelger S, Santesson S. Retorik för naturvetare: Skrivande som fördjupar lärandet. Lund: Studentlitteratur; 2012.
23. Phillips EM, Pugh DS. How to get a PhD: A handbook for students and their supervisors, 2nd Ed. Buckingham: Open University Press; 1994.